GW00381315

Linda M James is a writer of novels, non-fiction books and screenplays. She has had three books published and written two more. She's also had many short stories and poems published. In 2008 she was commissioned to write three screenplays: *Young Ivanhoe, Young Helen of Troy* and *Jesus Christ: The Missing Years. Young Ivanhoe* is being filmed in 2010.

Before becoming a writer, Linda was a model, a singer and an English Lecturer.

Her website is www.writingunderwater.co.uk

Also by the same author

Tempting The Stars (Vanguard Press)
ISBN: 978 184386 509 4

How to Write Great Screenplays (How To Books)
ISBN: 978 184528 307 0

The Invisible Piper

Linda M James

The Invisible Piper

Vanguard Press

VANGUARD PAPERBACK

A CIP catalogue record for this title is
available from the British Library.

ISBN 978 184386 508 7

Vanguard Press is an imprint of
Pegasus Elliot MacKenzie Publishers Ltd.
www.pegasuspublishers.com

First Published in 2009

Vanguard Press
Sheraton House Castle Park
Cambridge England

Printed & Bound in Great Britain

Dedication

To David, Andrew, Simon & Jamie

With my love

Acknowledgements

The author would like to thank the staff of the Imperial War Museum Library and Sound Archives; the Mass Observation Archives and Library at Sussex University, Brighton, and the Hastings Library and Museum for allowing her access to their books, documents, diaries, recordings and photographs.

The author would also like to thank Peters, Fraser and Dunlop for permission to quote from *Post Scripts,* J.B. Priestley's radio broadcasts in 1940.

The poem extract on page 155 comes from a book called *Truffle Eater* by Oistros. (Arthur Barker & Co, 1933)

'Everything is determined; the beginning, as well as the end, by forces over which we have no control... We all dance to an invisible tune intoned in the distance by an invisible piper.'

Einstein.
Saturday Evening Post.
26th October, 1929

Chapter 1

'Those who cannot remember
the past are condemned to repeat it.'

George Santayana
The Age of Reason, 1905

Rob distantly heard the telephone ring, but it couldn't have anything to do with him. He'd been flying for days without sleep.

He felt someone shaking him. 'Sir. Come on – another scramble.'

It was impossible. He'd only just gone to sleep. He staggered to his feet and headed for the door, fully clothed. He hadn't even taken off his flying boots; he'd been too exhausted after the last sortie. It was 4.30 a.m.

He saw the others running past him to their machines and suddenly, nervous energy flooded through his body. He ran towards his Spitfire, refuelled, rearmed and serviced in the short time since his last flight by the equally exhausted ground-crew.

The oscillating thunder of Merlin engines filled the air as pilots revved up. Rob could see the blue flames from the exhaust stubs, streaking through the half light.

'Up again, Sir? Don't them Jerries ever sleep?' Pickles, one of the ground-crew, yawned widely. 'Just oiled the canopy hood – bit stiff.'

Rob yawned back as he urinated on the grass: a practice which no longer embarrassed him since most of the other pilots did it to save time before sorties. He climbed into the cockpit.

Shaking the sleep away from his brain, he tested the oxygen supply and R/T and then taxied out to the far end of the aerodrome and turned into the wind. He saw the *thumps up* from Flight Commander 'Sandy' Lane and opened up. A throbbing roar filled the cockpit and cut off the outside world as he sped across the aerodrome. The bumps from the undercart became less and less, until with a final bump, he was off the deck and a grey blur of grass slipped beneath him. His right hand dropped to the undercart control and moved it back. Then he felt for the pump. A few seconds later, two faint thuds told him the wheels were up, only then did he reach behind him to pull the stiff hood shut. He stifled another yawn as he put the airscrew into course pitch, throttling back to cruising revs.

What the hell was he flying at 4.40 in the morning for? No sign of the bloody Hun.

A shiver ran across his body as the R/T crackled into life.

'Seventy plus Bandits approaching south-south-west. Angels 15 to 20.'

Rob looked around wildly, thankful he wasn't wearing a collar and tie. His neck had been rubbed raw for months until he'd taken to wearing roll neck sweaters and scarves, like most of the other pilots.

Then he saw them: thirty Dornier 17s and Ju 88 bombers at 15,000 feet, escorted by forty Me 109s at 20,000 feet.

Sandy's voice stabbed through the headphones.

'Go! Go! Go!'

Rob climbed steeply above one of the 109s and suddenly all he could see was hoar-frost covering his windscreen. No forward vision. His throat felt full of chalk. He watched the shaking in his hand as he rubbed a small section of screen. He had no idea where the 109 was. The oxygen was making him light-headed. It was a nightmare: trying to weave, scan his rear-view and clear the windscreen all at the same time. His breath came in short, agitated gasps as he broke away from the others and dived. At 10,000 feet the screen cleared.

Thank God. No Messerschmitt on my tail.

The air above the sea was misty so he didn't see the olive-green camouflage on the long thin Dornier 17 until tracers streamed past his cockpit.

Jesus!

He suddenly saw large, black swastikas on the fuselage of the Dornier 200 feet away and climbed at breakneck speed, the sweat pouring from him; his eyes searing the skies until he saw the enemy beneath him. He banked violently and the Dornier's starboard engine shot through his gun-sights. His thumb jammed down on the firing button and the Browning machine guns tore into the Dornier's engine. The bomber erupted into flames and screamed into the sea.

For a second, Rob relaxed back into his harness. Only a second. But a second he was going to regret, forever. A Messerschmitt was above him, coming out of the sun. He was blinded by the sudden blaze in his eyes; he didn't see the orange tracers stream towards him, just felt the violent *thump thump thump* of cannon shell screaming into his fuselage. He lost his elevator-control and the Spitfire went into a steep left-hand climbing turn. Rob felt the seat pressing deep into his body and momentarily blacked out. Then just as the pressure eased and the blood raced back through his brain, his oil tank burst into flames.

Terror electrified his body. He tore at the hood release. It wouldn't move. His screams filled the small cockpit as he watched flames eating through his fingers. Ignoring the pain, he tore again and again at the hood release. At last – it slammed back. He groped for the release pin securing the Sutton harness, trying to hold his head back from the flames. And suddenly, he was out, tumbling through sky and sea. A remote part of his brain told him to pull the ripcord: burning hands moved in slow motion towards the chromium ring; exposed nerve endings touched it and pulled.

His screams exploded around the sky as the white silk canopy billowed above him. He looked down at the roasted flesh at the end of his arms and gagged at the smell. Then suddenly, the shock came. He started to shake, uncontrollably, and soon his parachute was swaying crazily from side to side.

From a long distance away, he heard someone scream.

Chapter 2

'Evacuees have to accustom themselves to separation from family and friends, householders to sharing their homes with strangers ...'

Ernest Bevin
from a pamphlet entitled
Government Evacuation Scheme, 1939

It was a sunny morning in September 1939 and ten-year-old Charlie Slater was going on holiday for the first time in his life. He had a boxed gas mask around his neck, a brown paper parcel with a change of clothes hanging from a belt around his waist and a name-tag tied to the lapel of his short brown coat. He didn't notice the mothers fighting back their tears at Victoria Station as he was going to the seaside and had a slab of chocolate clutched in his sticky hand given to him by a woman on the evacuation committee. A whole slab. He charged up the steps of the train with eighty other children, desperate to get a window seat. He had never been on a train; had never seen the sea; had never eaten chocolate. The children cheered as the train steamed off. The mothers waved from the platform; some of the children remembered to wave back.

The train arrived at Hastings after a long, noisy journey. The teachers who had volunteered to accompany the children were exhausted after cleaning up vomit and urine from travel-sick and chocolate-gorged children. On top of this, they had to deal with a barrage of questions fired at them by children with strong stomachs and good bladder control:

'What's in that field, Miss? Is that a cow? Ugh! – ain't they ugly? – What's them dangly bits hanging like that for? Get a butcher's at the black one! What's she doin' on that cow's back, Miss?' 'Bit like me old man after the boozer,' piped up an older boy. 'Cor – look at all them white sheeps jumpin' about – how many lambs do they have a year?' 'Where can I have a Jimmy Riddle, Miss?' 'How long before we has a butcher's at the pigs you was telling us about?' 'Where's the houses and smoke gone, Miss? – there's nothin' here but grass!'

None of the children had ever been away from the streets of London for a day.

It was raining as a curve of children meandered down Havelock Road towards the new underground car park, following the middle-aged ladies who'd been sent to meet them. Suddenly the air was full of the anguished wail of an air-raid siren. Everyone started screaming. In the chaos that followed, many children tried gluing their bodies to wet pavements, while others stood in rigid shock, their fingers star-fished with tension. Only a handful of children, chocolate-smeared faces uplifted to the cutting edge of rain, stood in fearful excitement, desperate for their first sight of a large, black swastika on the side of an enemy aircraft. Charlie was one of them. Suddenly, they were all swept down the road by the adults and herded towards the safety of the underground car park. In the distance they saw an ARP warden wobbling towards them on an old bicycle shouting: 'False alarm! False alarm!' This false alarm, everyone discovered later, had been repeated all over England.

The children gasped as they walked into the car park: trestle tables lining the walls were piled high with food: tins of corned beef and spam, condensed milk and more slabs of milk chocolate. The air-raid warning was forgotten as they were each given a precious carrier bag full of food to take to their new homes.

They were steaming by the time they had walked from the car park to a large reception centre in a school hall where a committee of ladies were waiting with glasses of milk and Marie biscuits to welcome them. Charlie didn't like the smell of the hall; it reminded him of books. After the women had recovered from the shock of seeing eighty steaming children, most of whom were undernourished, sickly-looking and smelt, the hall slowly emptied as the host families took their evacuees. Only Charlie and a handful of equally scruffy boys were still there. He scanned the room, slanted with light from its six high windows, looking for someone in charge. He spotted a tall, thin, nervous woman who looked like a greyhound he'd seen racing in the dog track he'd gone to with his old man. She was standing in the corner of the hall, directing operations and twitching her hands in his direction. He walked over to her.

'Where's this woman's what's looking after me, then?'

Mrs Fraser, the billeting officer, forgot the fact that the Council had set up an extremely efficient evacuation scheme in which she was only a small cog. She'd watched five trainloads of children disgorge themselves into this hall for three days; she had worked extremely hard to ensure that all those children had a suitable family with which to be billeted. She was satisfied that she had everything sorted out satisfactorily – she had managed to make most families willingly agree to take an evacuee, but it had been difficult to convince others that they really needed one in their house. However, the fact that the government would pay 10/6d for one child under fourteen; 12/ 6d for one between fourteen and sixteen, and 8/6d each for two children, had obviously helped some of them change their minds.

She hadn't realised, of course, that the children would talk like Charlie or be quite so dirty.

'You listenin'? Where is she?'

She blinked in amazement at the boy and then looked quickly at his label. Charlie Slater: 114 Farleigh Road, Deptford. London. To: Dr & Mrs Adams: The Beeches, Pevensey Road, St Leonards-on-Sea. E. Sussex.

Oh dear, that couldn't be right. 'Er … hello, Charles. I'm afraid not all the ladies have arrived yet.'

'It's Charlie – why not?'

Mrs Fraser was horrified to see a small boy, at the other end of the hall, urinating down his leg onto the parquet floor.

'Why not?' Mrs Fraser repeated, blinking rapidly at the urinating child before rushing off to see if she could find Mrs Adams. She wasn't in the hall so Mrs Fraser went outside. There was Mrs Adams walking up the hill towards the school. Mrs Fraser tried to intercept her before she came into the hall.

'Yoohoo – Mrs Adams!'

Mary looked across the wet road reflecting the September trees and saw a very flustered Mrs Fraser standing at the entrance of the school hall. She crossed over just as a watery sun broke through the clouds.

'Sorry, I'm late, Mrs Fraser, but I've been very busy. My husband was on call again last night.'

'Oh, I quite understand – that's no problem, Mrs Adams – no problem at all.'

'Have the children arrived safely?'

'Oh yes, the children are safe all right, but … but …'

'Yes?'

'I'm afraid … I'm afraid … to be blunt, Mrs Adams – they're not what I expected.'

'What did you expect?'

'Well … nice children.'

'And aren't they?'

'Well – I'm sure some of them are, but… oh, you'll have to see for yourself.'

As they walked into the hall Mary was assaulted by the smell: although the hall had emptied considerably, the sour odour of damp, unwashed children still lingered in the air. Fierce battles were being fought between Stukka and Spitfire pilots as boys flew around the room blasting tracers at each other.

Mrs Fraser hopped from one foot to the other in embarrassment as she shouted above the noise. 'I'm terribly sorry, Mrs Adams. But I've been most dreadfully busy… I know you asked for a little girl, but all the little girls have gone, I'm afraid –'

Mrs Fraser spoke, Mary thought, as if she was trying to catch words that were running away from her.

'– if you could have come earlier this afternoon… you could have chosen… as it is… I'm afraid… er… Charles – the boy over there…'

Mrs Fraser pointed nervously at Charlie who was dive-bombing a Stukka, 'somehow has your name on his label and there aren't many children left and you did agree, didn't you?'

Mary looked from Charlie to Mrs Fraser in silence.

'Charles!' Mrs Fraser called across the room. Charlie roared towards the women, dive-bombing two more enemy in his path before taxiing to a noisy halt in front of them.

'Charles – I'd like you to meet Mrs Adams – your new foster mother.'

Mary looked in disbelief at the Cockney urchin standing in front of her who had a tuft of dingy looking hair sticking up from the back of his head: he was undersized, dirty and ragged, one of his eyes was almost closed with a large stye and his flesh had the grey, limp look of malnutrition. He reminded her of the Artful Dodger. She watched a trail of dirty snot drip down his upper lip. He licked it as it reached his mouth. Mary shuddered.

'I ain't Charles! – I's Charlie!' The boy peered up at Mrs Fraser who twittered at his side. 'You don't half talk funny.' He snorted with laughter as the women swallowed air.

Mary could feel a pulse throbbing at her left temple and unconsciously pressed her hand against it as she looked in amazement at the child. If indeed, he was a child.

'Are we goin' or what? Me legs is hurtin'.'

Mary could feel her mouth lock in an open position.

Mrs Fraser drew Mary aside. 'I've got nowhere else to take him, Mrs Adams… You can't imagine how difficult it is to place all the children we've been sent… I don't know whether I'm coming or going…'

'Mrs Fraser – I told you I wanted a little girl. Not a…' Mary couldn't think of an adequate word.

'So did everyone else, Mrs Adams. But the committee has been saying all the afternoon – "oh Mrs Adams will cope. Mrs Adams copes with everything." You always do, don't you? I don't know how you manage what with this and that. Between you and me, Mrs Adams, I really don't know why I agreed to take this job – it's really –'

'Mrs Fraser!'

The woman blinked rapidly at the staccato of Mary's voice and whispered. 'Please take him if only for a week or two until we can sort something out… Please!' Mrs Fraser clutched her arm tightly. Mary could feel her trembling at the thought of having to look after the boy herself.

'Oh, all right – a couple of weeks. But only a couple of weeks. Rob's coming home.'

Mrs Fraser almost danced the quick step. 'Oh thank you so much, Mrs Adams. I just knew you would.' She fluttered off down the hall, anxious to escape.

How could Mary have known that the boy would change her life for ever?

Charlie looked in awe at Mary's detached Victorian house with its impressive array of windows, black against the setting sun. 'Blimey – how many families live here, then?'

'Just one. Us.'

'Must have a lotta kids. Me Mum had six. Two's dead. How many you got?'

'One,' said Mary, completely out of her depth.

Charlie was almost speechless. 'One! With a house like this! You're havin' me on.'

'No,' Mary said carefully. 'I'm not. Now wipe your feet before you come in.'

But Charlie was looking at her front garden; at the beautiful russet beech trees, surrounded by a profusion of flowers: tall yellow hollyhocks, red and white carnations and pink roses.

'What's that pong?'

'My flowers.'

'Blimey – this your garden, then? – I thought it were a park or something. You must have a bob or two.'

Mary remembered her deep breathing exercises from her relaxation classes. She breathed deep from her abdomen. 'Come in, Charlie and meet Dr Adams.'

The Adams house was ruptured by Charlie's arrival; in one day he'd turned Mary's world upside down. Her husband John had shown her, she, who had never seen one nit before, approximately 2,000, all nestled in Charlie's hair.

'You can crack the big fellas with your nails. Me and me brother used to have a bet on who could crack the most in five minutes. I always won.' Mary looked at John in despair.

'I thought this sort of thing had died out with Dickens, John.'

'I've not seen such a crop since I was in the trenches.'

They sent Charlie outside to play in the garden while John contacted Mr Bruce, the Medical Officer, and warned him that they'd have to supply chemists with large quantities of Keatings to combat the vermin.

John was worried. 'What did the other children look like? As dirty as Charlie?'

'Well, it's difficult to tell – most of them seemed covered in quite a number of things.'

'Oh Lord – I think we've got a health crisis on our hands. As if I haven't got enough to cope with. We'll have to bath the boy straight away.'

'We? I can cope with most things, but not verminous children, I'm afraid.'

'Verminous? He's the "bud of the nation."'

'What are you talking about?' Mary asked.

'Our Minister of Health, Ernest Brown, my dear, on the wireless the other night, talking about the advantages of having an evacuee in one's home.'

'Oh really – I wonder how many he's got in his house.'

'And I thought you could cope with anything.'

'Yes, well – don't gloat or you won't have any dinner.'

'Is that a threat or a promise?'

Their cook Betty had just enlisted in the ATS so Mary, who was a mediocre cook, was forced back into the kitchen. John was still trying to digest last evening's meal of uncooked potatoes and over-cooked pork.

Mary went into the kitchen to wrestle with a new recipe of corned beef and cabbage while John took Charlie upstairs. She suddenly heard the boy screaming at the top of his voice and went running up the stairs to the bathroom. He was rigid against the wall with tears pouring down his face.

'He's tryin' to drown me, he is! He wants me to take me things off and then – and then – he's goin' to push me under the water. I heard about men like him.'

The boy was shaking with fear and holding on to his threadbare clothes as if his life depended on it. He stared at the water as if mesmerised. Mary's eyes followed his fear.

'He's never seen a bath before, John.'

'What?' John looked at her in amazement. 'Don't be ridiculous.'

Mary knelt down in front of the boy, although his rancid smell made her feel nauseous.

'Charlie – Dr Adams and I go in the water once a week to get off our dirt.'

Charlie dragged his eyes away from the water to Mary's face.

'But you ain't got no dirt.'

'That's because we have a bath every week … If you had a bath you wouldn't have any dirt either.'

Charlie looked stunned by this sudden knowledge. 'You mean he ain't tryin' to drown me?'

Mary stopped herself from smiling. 'No, Charlie. He's trying to get you clean.'

'But I's always dirty – and me Mum's sewed me up for the winter.'

'Sewed you up?'

Charlie shivered as he opened his thin shirt; underneath they could see a layer of brown paper next to his skin. Mary and John looked at each other.

'Yeah – bugs can't get through the paper see. Me Mum says.'

'I've got something better than paper to stop the bugs getting you, Charlie.'

He stopped shaking. 'What's that then?'

'It's called a vest.'

Charlie looked at her dubiously. 'Yeah – but can it stop you coughin' up blood? I never coughed up none 'cos I'm sewn up, see – but me brother – Mum didn't have enough paper so he weren't sewn up – and he died.'

Mary could feel her eyes pricking as she walked out of the room.

Charlie shouted after her. 'So he ain't gonna drown me, then?'

'No, Charlie – he's quite safe,' she called back.

Chapter 3

'The most persistent sound which reverberates through man's history is the beating of war drums.'

Arthur Koestler
Janus. A Summing Up. Prologue, 1935

The truck swung heavily around a corner. In the back, sitting on the floor facing each other, sat ten men dressed as civilians. They instinctively pressed their shoes hard against the metal floor to avoid touching each other. They were being driven seventy miles away from their base in Stratford-upon-Avon where they were all doing their Initial Training for the RAF.

Sergeant Brown was a regular soldier whose pinched face had the ferret alertness of a small rodent. He had been trying for weeks to "change a rabble into a fighting force". The RAF was taking anyone now there was a war on, he told them repeatedly. Leaning forward to give them yet more last-minute instructions, he said:

'Remember – you're on your own. This is supposed to be enemy territory. No dropping in for a cuppa and a map from the locals to get back to base, remember.'

'We're hardly going to do that now, are we, Sarge? – not after you've told everyone for seventy miles we're escaped Germans! That would be bloody daft, wouldn't it?' Dai Jones, a small, compact Welshman, made the Sergeant feel as if someone was rubbing his skin with sandpaper.

'Oh is that a fact, boyo – well if you're so fuckin' clever you'll get back first, won't you?'

Rob looked at Colin as they swayed around another corner. They had heard all this before.

'Don't use the King's shilling to telephone unless it's a matter of life and death. Death in the case of Jones here,' continued the Sergeant.

They laughed on cue. Rob kicked Dai's foot just as he was going to reply.

The truck abruptly stopped for the first pair to get out. They drove off to the next point of dispersal. This procedure continued three times until it was Colin and Rob's turn. Colin had been friends with Rob since grammar school, ever since Rob had blitzed two bullies in the playground. They had been taunting Colin for weeks for having carrot-coloured hair. No one had noticed his hair colour after the fight.

Rob and Colin had decided to go to the same University, but had left immediately when war had been declared. They had volunteered for the RAF; both determined to become fighter pilots. But first they had to endure Kingo exercises.

'Right – the Siamese twins next. Good luck, gentlemen. See you before breakfast. Don't get caught by the locals. The farmers might shoot you.' Sergeant Brown bellowed with laughter at the thought before the truck drove off, leaving them in a trail of fumes and dirt.

They had been dropped off in a wood in the middle of nowhere. It was only 5 o'clock, but it was already getting dark. The silence was startling after the noisy movement of the truck. They listened to it for some moments until it was interrupted by the *stip stip stip shreee* of wood warblers in a nearby oak. They watched a blur of yellow flash past them into the gathering gloom.

'God – if only I'd been born a bird. How the hell does ferret-face think we're going to get back to base without a compass?' Colin looked around at the mass of dark shadowed trees and dirt paths surrounding them. 'And I'm starving. God, I could be eating some of my old Mum's jam tarts right now if it wasn't for Hitler.'

'Oh, stop moaning. Think,' Rob said.

There was a long silence.

'Well, nothing springs immediately to mind, Einstein.'

'Ever heard of navigation by the stars?' Rob was elated as he looked up at the sharp pinpricks of light which were swiftly becoming the only focal point.

'Oh, very biblical. And which star is going to guide us to the stable?'

'Listen pea-brain, while you were chatting up girls after school, I was studying astronomy … look up there – where's the North Pole star?'

'Haven't a clue.'

'What! An A in Physics and he doesn't know where the North Pole star is! Look up – can you see the Plough?'

'Of course I can see the bloody Plough! … it's … don't know.'

'Christ – you did have an eye test when you enlisted, didn't you? Watch my finger … over to your left … Okay? Seven stars in a cluster which look like a plough … Got it? Now take the two end stars and follow up with your eye until you get to the North Pole Star – Polaris – a second-magnitude star that never sets.'

'What?' said Colin, cricking his neck as he looked up at the star-laden sky. A sudden gust of wind cut into his face sharply.

'The second brightest star in the sky.'

'Okay, thanks for the lecture. So how do we get to base?'

'Base is due east. We keep the North Pole Star on our left and Bob's your Uncle.' Rob looked up at the galaxies of worlds he'd always wanted to touch as a boy.

'Why didn't you bloody say so before? Come on – I'm starving.'

They were walking along a completely black road, not a house light to be seen because of the blackout, when they suddenly heard the sound of a middle-aged man's voice in the distance.

'Fan out all of you, we don't want them to catch us in a pincer movement.'

'Christ – it's the local Vigilante group!' whispered Colin.

'They haven't heard us and they can't possibly see us,' Rob whispered back. 'Damn – we're only a couple of miles away from base as well – let's get off the road – fast. What's that over there?' They both peered through the blackness.

'Can't make out a thing. Let's run for it, anyway.'

They ran straight into a stone wall. Their roars of pain shook the ten farmers who were desperately tired of looking for spies in the dark. Suddenly the air was full of whistles and shouting and running feet.

A light flooded out from a nearby farmhouse and silhouetted Colin and Rob's concussed confusion before someone shouted "Put that light out!" Two farm dogs raced towards them and sank their teeth into their ankles just before the farmers attacked them with pitchforks.

After four hours of questioning by the local police and a phone call to the base, they were released into the hands of an astonished Sergeant Brown: their clothes stank with the copious amounts of manure they had fallen into outside the farmyard; their faces were ballooning from their impact with the wall and starting to discolour, and they were limping from the attack by the dogs. The Sergeant shook his head as he turned to the police.

'And these are the sort of lads what are going to win the war for us.'

'Bloody hell!' one of the policemen said. 'Better start learning German – quick!'

The men roared with laughter as Rob and Colin limped off into the night.

Chapter 4

'It is vital that a passenger search his conscience before making a railway journey. It is more than ever vital to ask yourself is my journey really necessary?'

World War II
Ministry of Information Poster

Charing Cross Station on a freezing morning in December 1939 was packed with a knot of pushing people: khaki-clad servicemen hauling large kitbags mingled with Air Force blue; civilians dragging large suitcases; mothers hanging onto screaming children and hundreds of gas masks in boxes draped over hundreds of shoulders. The stream of people trying to get out were pushed back by a tidal wave trying to get in.

Colin and Rob were going home on leave. They eventually managed to fight their way into the station, hampered by enormous kitbags. They were immediately hit by the noise and smell of a busy station that had a constant flood of people flowing in and out every minute of the day. Their eyes smarted with the combination of sulphurous fumes of smoke hissing out of trains, and dust blowing up from the empty tracks and unswept stone platforms. In the distance they saw a small woman pushing a tea wagon, mounted with a nickel urn and piled with a mountain of dry, yellow buns that looked as if they had been baked before the war.

'Stale buns,' drooled Colin. 'I'm slowly dying of hunger.'

A small boy with dirty, knobbly knees was stalking the tea lady, waiting for the moment when he could accidentally knock over one of the tea-stained china cups, balancing precariously on top of her trolley. His harassed mother ran over to him and clipped his ear before dragging him off. His face went rigid with rage.

Colin and Rob had just managed to get near the tea lady when they heard the distorted voice of a Tannoy:

'Platform 4 for the 10.30 train to Hastings. Calling at Waterloo, London Bridge, Orpington –'

'Forget your stomach. Come on!' Rob shouted as he rushed towards the platform.

'– Wadhurst, Stonegate, Etchingham, Robertsbridge, Battle, West St Leonards, St Leonards-Warrior Square and Hastings –'

'Every bloody station. God knows what time we'll get home.'

'Never mind – just think of their faces when they see us.' Rob squeezed past a husband and wife with three small children who were in various stages of temper tantrums.

'Christ – give me a plane anytime.' Colin looked in horror at the distorted faces of the petulant children. He was struggling with his heavy kitbag slung over one shoulder, only managing to carry it by walking at an angle of sixty degrees. Rob, on the other hand, with all the self-assurance Colin had always envied in school, looked as if he'd been born carrying his.

'Bloody Bedlam!' Rob said, fighting his way onto platform four.

As soon as they got to the platform their nostrils were filled with another smell: the acrid scent of corridors and carriages that were used too much and cleaned too little. An enormously fat woman elbowed her way past them, followed by a grey wisp of a man who occupied the tiny space she left in her wake. Her husband was swept along by the crowd pushing him from behind. He protested feebly.

'Follow the battleship,' Rob said. 'She'll find some space.'

'Thank God she's on our side.' Colin moved his kitbag onto his other shoulder, almost knocking a young pretty WAAF officer over in the process. 'Oh – sorry.'

She smiled at him briefly before being swept away by the crowd.

'Damn!'

'Come on, Col – no time for that – we've got to get on that train.' Rob manoeuvred himself behind the battleship.

'Are you following me, Harold?' the battleship boomed to her husband, her enormous beige coat flapping in his face.

'Yes, dear.'

'I see a seat!'

So did everyone else. There was a stampede as everyone ran for it. The enormous woman was at the head of the queue and was pushed forcibly from behind. She became wedged in the doorway: her buttocks blocking the door.

'Do something. Harold!' she screamed.

Harold scratched his nose.

The sight of the buttocks overflowing around the door was too much for the crowd. Forgetting that only a minute earlier they'd been prepared to trample each other underfoot for the now unobtainable seat, they started to laugh.

'Who needs Charlie Chaplin when you can see a sight like that!' shouted one wag from the crowd.

Colin dropped his kitbag to the ground. 'Rob, look at her husband's face.'

The grey wisp of a man, far from trying to help his wife, was leaning against the carriage. He suddenly produced an enormous cigar from inside his coat like a magician, lit it, and blew out a perfect smoke ring.

'Harold – what are you doing?' screamed his hysterical wife.

'Nothing as yet, my petal.' Then Harold suddenly crouched under his wife's buttocks and gave an almighty heave. The woman was propelled into the lap of a small clergyman who had been quietly ignoring the proceedings by concentrating on his *Times*. He went white under the weight.

After four hours, the atmosphere in the carriage was fetid with the smell of unwashed bodies, socks stinking with days of marching, smoke and the lingering bittersweet smell of a child's vomit; her mother hadn't been able get her to the toilet quickly enough as two service men were trying to sleep there. Colin and Rob, like many others, were standing in one of the long corridors with not even a view to look at since they had pasted over most of the windows with gummed paper to stop the glass shattering in case of aerial attack. They looked enviously at the seated occupants of the nearest carriage: the small vicar, still reading his *Times*; a trio of old ladies, dressed in black sateen, snored sedately with their mouths slightly open; two soldiers, who'd taken off their boots, accompanied them with a raucous bass rumble; and the battleship, whose buttocks spread to fill half the long carriage seat, forcing the soldiers into pungent proximity. But even standing for hours couldn't dampen Rob's and Colin's excitement.

'Spitfires, Col! We could be flying them in a couple of weeks.'

'Yeah – after all the bloody months of drilling and doing hundred of things with a rifle except fire it.'

'And getting drunk and going out with women.'

'Well, there was that, I suppose,' Colin conceded. The train jerked to a halt with a loud hiss of steam. The old ladies and soldiers woke up with a start and looked through the murky windows for a familiar landmark.

'What a nuisance,' muttered the clergyman who had now recovered sufficiently from his attack to be able to speak. 'I've just read that the authorities are going to remove all road and railway signs from every station.'

'Well, we don't want to give the Germans landmarks when they invade, do we, Vicar?' The battleship's eyes flashed patriotically. 'We all have to put up with inconvenience in war time, you know.'

'Yes, yes, yes, Madam … I know that. But how will one know when to get off?'

'You could always ask God, Vicar,' the grey wisp of a husband said, seeming to grow less grey with every mile he travelled. He sat on the floor of the carriage munching a spam sandwich, oblivious to the pungent smell of sweaty feet. His wife looked down at him in astonishment.

The vicar became flustered. 'My dear fellow – one can't ask for God's help on such trivial matters … I mean what if everyone asked for such help? God can't listen to everyone.'

The little man stared at the vicar for some time. 'Who does he listen to exactly? Is it only the British or has he got time to listen to Germans as well?'

Everyone leaned forward, wanting to hear the vicar's answer. Rob was thinking of Axel, his German pen friend, with whom he'd stayed for so many summers in North Germany. He wondered if he had enlisted in the Luftwaffe.

The vicar flushed as he fingered his dog collar. 'I really don't think that this is the time or the place to have a theological discussion.'

'But they're important questions, aren't they?' Colin asked as he sat on his kitbag at the door of the carriage. 'Is it possible for God to be on both sides in a war?'

The vicar started to perspire in the airless compartment as they all pinned him with their eyes. 'Dear, oh dear – it's not for us to question the workings of God. He moves in mysterious ways.' He mopped his forehead with a large white handkerchief.

'You're not answering the question, Vicar.' The little grey man looked positively pink in the reflection of his wife's astonished eyes. 'Whose side is God on?'

'Ahh!' – The vicar scanned the station again. 'I believe this is my station.' He gulped in fetid air. 'Another time, perhaps,' and gathering his belongings together quickly, he opened the carriage door and hopped off the train.

They all stared out of the window as he almost ran along the platform.

The little man chuckled. '"Lord, now lettest thou thy servant depart in peace."' He looked at Colin and Rob, pointing to the now vacant seat. 'Mine I think you'll agree,' and smartly sat down. 'I think I'll have another spam sandwich now, dear.'

'Of course, Harold – have them all,' answered his amazed wife, passing him all the food.

'Well, religion certainly seems to have worked miracles for him,' Colin murmured to Rob. 'A seat and food ... that vicar couldn't answer the question, could he?'

'How can it be answered?' Rob responded.

Chapter 5

'The British Housewife is helping to make a second front – the Kitchen Front – against Hitler. That is why we say "Medals for you, Madam," Is there anything else you can do?'

World War II
Ministry of Food Poster

Hilda looked at her raw hands, rough from years of washing up dirty dishes in a scullery where the sun always had to fight to find a space on the floor. It had to fight even harder now the windows were criss-crossed with sticky tape. Why did Hitler have to invade Poland? Why did he have to have more territory? She scoured a pan vigorously as she tried to understand what was happening to the world. And Stalin bombing Helsinki – how could you justify bombing a city? All the suffering the Polish and Finnish people must have endured. All the senseless cruelty and hatred. What for? The awful futility of it all. It made her head hurt.

She felt the sweat trickle down between her large breasts. It was clammy in the small back room, even on a cold day like this. She looked down at her swollen ankles bulging over her ugly lace-up shoes – the only shoes she could wear these days – and remembered the days when her ankles were small. She sighed as she studied the dishes – no matter how many times she washed the plates there were always smears. But what could you do with wartime detergent? All these restrictions coming in. Then she suddenly smiled as she remembered Tommy Handley on the wireless in the new *ITMA* programme, joking about 700 new Government restrictions: no kisses on Wednesdays, no baths on Thursdays and no hanky-panky on Fridays … it went on.

He made it all seem funny.

'Mum – do I have to wear my gymslip. Kate doesn't!' Rose came hurtling down the stairs, threw herself into her mother's ample, warm body and soaked up her mother's smell – a mixture of lavender, bicarbonate of soda and sweat. Rose loved it. She stroked her mother's lined face with sticky fingers.

'Tell me the story about when you were living in the big house in Catsfield and all the gentlemen were dressed in pink and there were dogs everywhere and all the servants had to bring them brandy to warm them up before –'

'You've heard it a hundred times, now go and wash your fingers, put your gym-slip on and come and eat your porridge. Now!'

Hilda watched the small rigid body stomp up the stairs. 'I wish I was as old as Kate then I wouldn't look like a brown beetle. All I need is a shell!'

Hilda smiled, remembering the day she had named her 'Rose' because she had looked just like one; all the nurses had said they had never seen such a flower before. Now look at her – more like a dandelion caught in the wind. Hilda could feel Rose's movements across the bedroom floor. She sighed.

'Oh for goodness sake – stop banging!' shouted Kate, her seventeen-year-old daughter, from upstairs. 'You know you have to wear it, so why make a fuss every morning.'

'Because I hate brown! Why can't I wear green?'

Bill dragged himself into the scullery, looking drawn from all the Civil Defence meetings he had to go to after work, just as Hilda finished the last dish. Too tired herself last night to wash them. Things had slipped since the war started.

'Hilda – tell that child to stop that racket!'

Perhaps it was the dreary light in the room, but she wondered if she looked as grey as her husband; if she had aged that much in one year.

'What's the matter with the child? Why's she always making a fuss about something?'

'Sit down and have your porridge, love. It's her age I expect.' She sat down heavily opposite Bill, glad to take the weight of her swollen feet.

'Her age! – our Colin and Katherine was never like that … When's his course finish?'

'I don't know, they're not supposed to write things like that, are they? Censor wouldn't like it.'

'Oh don't be so daft, woman – he could tell us when he's got leave.' He suddenly clamped his hand to his left ear. 'Oh bloody hell – it's starting again.'

Hilda got up and went over to the stove. She still had some pith left over from the ash twigs she'd heated yesterday.

'You need some more – I'll warm it up.'

'I wonder sometimes if your mother's remedies work.'

Hilda turned to look at her husband's truculent face.

'Don't you want it then?'

'Oh, I suppose so, but be quick – I've got to open the shop.'

Hilda warmed the fluid before pouring it into her husband's ear and plugging it with cotton wool. They heard Kate above them in the bedroom, shouting at her sister again.

'Every morning it's the same,' Bill said, wiping his ear. 'It's getting on my nerves, Hilda. You've let Rose run riot – that's the trouble.'

Hilda walked over to the sink to wash her hands. 'There wasn't a war on when the others were little. Why don't you say something to her if it bothers you so much.'

'Me? That's your department that is … where's the sugar?'

She dreaded telling him but what could she do? 'Queued for hours yesterday. None of the shops had any left … Anyway we've used up our rations.' He dropped his spoon into the porridge in disgust as she sat down opposite him.

'Porridge without sugar! It's – it's –'

'Inedible?' Kate bounded into the room, her skin glowing. Hilda wondered how she managed to look so fresh; she never seemed to worry about anything. Hilda couldn't remember the last time she'd had a proper sleep.

'Any jam, Mum?' Hilda nodded. 'I'll get it.' Kate walked into the dank pantry, which grew bluish-grey mould on its walls. Her face wriggled up as the smell hit her. 'You could grow that new penicillin in there. It's awful.'

'Well, it's a good job you don't have to go in there often then, isn't it, Miss? It's lucky for you, you don't have to queue up for things like I do,' retorted Hilda. 'You can bury yourself in books at school, can't you?'

Kate took in her mother's tight face. What have I done wrong now? She thought. Then suddenly, Rob's face was in front of her. She flushed with the memory of their last meeting. He must be coming home for leave soon. She sat down quickly and bent over her toast quickly to avoid her mother's prying eyes.

Hilda got up slowly from the table and shouted for Rose to come down. She came stomping into the room and threw herself noisily into a chair.

'Can't you ever come into a room quietly?' her father grumbled, his ear still hurting.

'No!'

Bill's face mottled with anger. 'Will you listen to this child, Hilda – talking to her father like that! My father would of got out his belt to me if I'd spoke to him like that.'

'Oh, not your father again,' Rose said, kicking the table.

'Rose!' Hilda looked from her daughter's to her husband's taut lips.

'I blame you, Hilda! If you'd disciplined this child proper she'd never answer me back. Our Colin and Katherine never spoke to me like that – never. What was the point in me fighting my way through the last war? What for, eh? To work all day in a shop – meetings all night and come home to get cheek from a ten-year-old child.' He scraped his chair back and stood up. 'I'll not stand for it.'

'Then sit down,' Rose said, banging her legs harder against the chair legs.

'What?' he thundered at her, holding his ear against the sudden pain.

Rose shrank in her chair. The sound of Bill's laboured breathing filled the scullery before he stormed out; his body an arrow of anger.

'Bill!' Hilda called after him. 'Don't forget your identity card if you're –'

Her voice trailed off as the front door slammed.

The only sound in the room for a long time was the dripping of the large old tap in the sink.

'Why do you talk to your father like that, Rose?' Hilda was genuinely troubled by her younger daughter who had changed so much in the last year. She could hardly recognise the child who used to wait for her father to come back from the shop and tell her stories before she went to sleep.

'Dunno.' Rose pulled on the hem of her gymslip until some of the stitches came loose.

'Don't do that! – I've only just sewed it up!' Hilda shouted.

Rose's face crumpled. 'I'm sorry, Mum.' She rushed over to her mother and buried her face in her breasts. 'I don't mean to – it just comes out.'

'Puberty, I expect, Mum,' said Kate.

Hilda's eyes burned Kate's face. 'And you'd know all about that, wouldn't you? What with your spots.'

Chapter 6

'Give me a home, not a house.'

James Carlisle
The Feather Bed, 1906

Rob and Colin arrived at Hastings Railway Station late in the afternoon. They'd fallen asleep on their kit-bags and had overshot the Warrior Square station. Walking against the wind towards the town centre they saw the Albert Memorial Clock Tower: a meeting place for their school friends ever since they were in the Grammar school. Rob looked up at the Portland stone statue of Prince Albert, austere in his robes as Knight of the Garter. Above him was the large clock Rob had used as a timepiece since he was a small boy. It was running five minutes late as usual. Even in wartime there were still some things you could rely on thought Rob, smiling.

He looked across the road towards the sea. It was a pale grey-blue, almost white, the same colour as the sky, shifting with small, luminous, dancing movements as the wind blew over it. Colin followed his gaze.

'Still wet then,' said Colin looking around for the bus. 'It's bloody freezing.'

Rob looked up as enormous yellow-beaked gulls swooped over them, screeching raucously. He hadn't noticed how much a part of his life they were until he had lived so long inland. He breathed deeply.

'Wonderful … the sound of the gulls and the smell of the sea.'

'Oh, Christ! – you're not coming over poetic, are you?' said Colin. 'Bugger the sea. I want some of my old Mum's Viennese rolls. Come on – here's the bus and for Christ's sake don't talk like that when we get back to the Mess – they'll crucify you.' They climbed on the trolley bus and everyone turned round to stare at them.

Two small boys with eyes like saucers jumped up when they saw Rob and Colin's blue uniforms under their greatcoats and gave them their seats.

'Wow! – flyers!'

Colin and Rob looked at each other and grinned, flattered by the light that fell on them from the boys' faces.

The bus conductor wouldn't let them pay any fare.

'Your lot's going to win us the war, lads,' he said as the bus trundled off on its scenic route along the sea road. He turned to the other passengers. 'Isn't that right, folks!'

Everyone nodded and smiled, wanting to shake their hands before they left the bus. Rob leaned over and whispered to Colin.

'I feel like the Pope.'

'Bloody hell – we'll be signing autographs next,' whispered Colin as he shook an old lady's hand before helping her off the bus.

'God bless you, son,' she said before hobbling off.

'Remember a white-haired old woman on the bus two summers ago, Rob, just like her – calling us a "disgrace to the grammar school" for larking around? Hitler's done a lot for our image, hasn't he?'

The trolley bus trundled along Eversfield Place towards St. Leonards. Towering above the Victorian buildings in the distance, Rob saw the Marina Court; a multi-storied white building built like the superstructure of a liner, looking as if it was steaming towards them. He'd watched it being built five years earlier and had hated it. His mother had written to tell him that it had been taken over as an Initial Training Centre. Why on earth they had been sent to Stratford-upon-Avon when they could have trained here was beyond him. Colin nudged him. Service men were drilling on the promenade surrounded by a gaggle of children imitating their rigid postures.

'Poor sods,' Colin said.

Rob stared at the sea, bathed in winter light. Two boys were throwing strands of dark seaweed at each other on the shore and laughing. The shingle was just as he and Kate had left it last summer.

He walked past St. John's Church where he used to be a choir boy. He loved the stability of its roundel tower and spire, recalling the sound of its bells creeping into his dreams each Sunday morning, reminding him to get up and be holy. It wasn't that long ago. As he crossed the road the Gothic arch of the North Lodge came into view; the house where Sir Rider Haggard had lived for many years. Rob smiled as he remembered the nights when he'd read his book *King Solomon's Mines* under the bedclothes with the aid of a torch when he should have been sleeping.

He walked along the sweep of Pevensey Road, soaking up the feeling of space that the wide road gave him with its avenue of cherry trees and large, tall Victorian buildings. There was a sound of screaming coming from his house a hundred yards away – as if someone was being killed. In spite of the weight of his kitbag he started running. When he opened the heavy front door, his nostrils wrinkled as a strong smell of disinfectant hit him. He heard a boy yelling upstairs.

'I ain't goin' in it! I ain't goin'!'

'Mum?' Rob dropped his kitbag and ran up the stairs. He saw a small, thin boy with very short, spiky hair flattened against the wall of the guest room, shouting the same words over and over. The smell of disinfectant was even stronger in this room. Mary turned to him in astonishment and shouted over the noise.

'Robbie, darling. Thank God you've come. Your father's been called out again and I can't do anything with him.'

'Is this the boy you wrote about?' Rob shouted back. 'I thought he was only staying a –'

'Yes, so did I.' Mary suddenly noticed his uniform. 'Oh darling – you look so handsome.'

Charlie noticed it too and stopped screaming.

'You a flyer?'

'Yes. Who are you?'

'Charlie Slater. Who are you?'

'Robert Adams.'

'Oh – Mrs Adams' boy.'

Rob smiled. 'I suppose I am.' He turned to his mother. 'I thought someone was being strangled.'

'So do the neighbours. They keep coming around because of the noise.'

Rob had never seen his mother so upset before. He turned to the boy shivering in his striped pyjamas. 'What's the matter? Why are you screaming?'

'Your Mum wants me to lie down on the bed and put this white thing round me and I ain't doin' it!'

Rob looked at his mother who shrugged her shoulders in incomprehension.

'It's the same every night – he insists on sleeping under the bed.'

Rob looked at Charlie's rigid body. 'Perhaps I can have a talk to Charlie alone, Mum … Do you want to know about flying, Charlie?'

He watched Charlie's face light up like a Very light. 'Yeah!'

Rob kissed his mother's cheek before she left the bedroom.

Charlie looked at him suspiciously. 'You ain't a iron hoof, is you?'

'What?'

'A pouf.'

Rob laughed. 'Don't think so.' He looked around the small room, noticing that patches of the red-flocked wallpaper had been torn off the wall in various places. 'I used to sleep here sometimes when I was your age.'

'Your Mum showed me your room. It's gotta big thing in it.'

Rob looked at him. 'What? – Oh, you mean my telescope … You mustn't touch that.'

'Why'd you sleep in here? Your room's as big as a dog track.'

'Not quite. And it's on the other side of the house – away from my parents' room and sometimes I used to get frightened in the night.'

Charlie looked incredulously at Rob. 'Frightened? What of?'

'Oh, all sorts of things. Ghosts. Trees blowing in the wind. Nightmares. School. I was scared of a lot of things when I was your age.'

'Well I ain't. I's scared of nothing!' He looked up at Rob, ready for an argument.

Rob sat on the bed without speaking.

'What about the flying, then? You said you gonna tell me.'

'I will, but you have to tell me something first.'

'What?'

'Why you won't get into bed.'

There was a long silence as Charlie studied the floor intently.

'Okay.' Rob got up and walked towards the door, then turned back. 'I'm going to be flying Spitfires soon.'

'Spits! What you gonna fly? Mark 1s?'

Rob shook his head.

Charlie looked at him for at least a minute.

'You won't say nothing to no-one?'

'About what?'

'About … about … I ain't slept in a bed.'

'Never?'

'Naw – we only got one, see – me and me brothers always sleep under Mum and Dad's. It's all right … ghosts don't look under beds an' … an' I ain't wearin' those friggin' white things!'

'What white things?'

Charlie pointed to the sheets on his bed.

'Why not?'

'Cause that's what you put people in when they die in the night and I ain't gonna die.'

'What?'

'Me Grandad and me Nan were put in one of them and they died. I seen them.'

Mary, John and Rob were sitting in the lounge listening to Brahms' Piano Concerto No. 2 on the gramophone. The elegant room with its high Victorian ceilings and deep windows was freezing in spite of a roaring fire in the small Victorian grate. Two tapestry screens depicting the hunt of Diana were draped around the door and windows in a vain attempt to stop the December draughts. They were finishing off a bottle of Chablis Premier Cru that John had been saving for such an occasion. He had just returned from the surgery and was trying to disguise his exhaustion.

'What happened to the wallpaper, Mum?' Rob saw his mother's eyebrows lift.

'Charlie told me that you have to look under the wallpaper to check for bugs. That's what his mother does whenever they are forced to move because they can't pay the rent. It seems his family has moved a great deal.'

'I didn't know people were that poor. Not these days,' Rob said, draining his glass. He walked over to a small mahogany table where his father had left the bottle and poured himself another.

John stared into the fire for some time before speaking. 'You can't imagine the problems we've had with the evacuees, Rob – constant bed-wetting, malnutrition, skin disorders, head-lice.'

Mary shuddered at the thought of Charlie's infested hair. 'The Catholic Women's League set up washing parties for weeks to clean the children's heads.'

'It's unbelievable,' Rob said.

John looked across the room at his son. 'I went up to London for the Lister Memorial Lecture last month. We were told that sodium hypochlorite is the ideal antiseptic because of its germ killing and cleansing powers. Then I went to see Charlie's parents. They have one room for eating, one room for sleeping, Rob. They haven't enough money to feed and clothe themselves, let alone four children. They'd need a bucket load of sodium hypochlorite to clean the place. And yet they can't afford to go to the doctors.' John's face furrowed in the firelight. 'I wonder how many people don't come to see me because they can't afford it. When you go to London, Rob, go to Charlie's neighbourhood, it'll open your eyes. It certainly opened mine.'

'Haven't Charlie's parents come to see him?'

'What with?'

Rob looked at his father for a long time. 'It must be hard for him to adapt to us, mustn't it?'

'Hard for him? I don't know why my hair isn't completely white.' Mary turned to John. 'Every day is traumatic, isn't it?'

'Remember he's had no discipline or been to school much.'

'Why not?' Rob asked him.

'Schooling doesn't seem very important when you're suffering from malnutrition, Rob. Did you know some of the parents of evacuated children have taken them back to London already? There are no schools open in some areas, so the children just wander the streets with nobody looking after them.' John's face looked grey with worry.

'Don't take up another cause, please darling. You do enough as it is – you can't change the world all by yourself.'

'Mum's right, Dad.' Rob was worried by the greyness in his father's face.

'I was rather hoping you might help me, my dear,' John said, smiling at his wife.

Rob looked at his parents smiling at each other, and not for the first time, felt deeply envious of their rapport.

'Anyway, we've got to celebrate. Rob's home. John turned to Rob and raised his glass. 'To Robert. Our embryo flyer.'

'To Robert,' Mary repeated, smiling at her son, noticing how much his face had changed since he'd been away. He'd always been lean since he was fifteen and done athletics, but now there were angles in his face she hadn't seen before: as if every muscle had been sculpted.

'This really is a good wine, Dad.'

'Isn't it, though? I'll have to lay down some more for the next celebration.'

'Pity you didn't have any more children, you two,' Rob said, 'you could celebrate more often.' A hot lump of coal spat out onto the carpet. Rob jumped up and threw it quickly onto the fire with the tongs, missing the quick look of pain *that* passed between his parents.

'You'd never believe what the training was like, Mum – I've never cleaned so many buttons, washed so many floors or marched so many miles before – and I had to share a room with fifteen unwashed men.'

'Oh, darling,' Mary was horrified, 'how awful – Didn't they have enough baths?'

Rob and John smiled at each other.

'It's wartime training, Mary. He's not made of pastry, my dear –'

'No problem if it was Mum's – just fire it at the Hun and they'd retreat immediately.'

The men roared with laughter.

'The best secret war weapon we have,' John said, wiping the tears from his eyes.

'Well – why don't you two try making it sometime if it's so awful.' Mary was hurt.

'Oh, my dear – we're only teasing – this is the first good laugh I've had in weeks.'

'Remember Dad's face, Mum – when his dentures got stuck in the crust?' Rob collapsed back into the chair, helpless.

Soon Mary was laughing too, remembering the shock on John's face. She looked at her husband and son laughing in the flickering firelight and suddenly, a terrible fear flooded her body.

Colin felt a deep well of loneliness wash over him. Silence was the only thing that greeted him when he opened the door of his parents' terraced house. He hadn't expected to find his mother or the girls out. He went straight into the pantry and found some of his mother's home-made bread, plastered it with margarine and jam and sat down in the murky scullery to wait in the gathering shadows, drawing his greatcoat around him for warmth.

'Why can't we get brighter lights, Mum – I can't hardly see,' Rose moaned, walking into the gloomy hall with its forty-watt bulb.

Colin smiled. No change there then.

'Because there's a war on. We must save electricity. How many times do I have to –'

'Mum!' Colin called out.

'Oh my giddyaunt!' Hilda felt quite faint as she walked into the scullery and saw her son. She held onto the table. 'Our Colin – why didn't you tell me you was coming, love? I'd have baked all day. You should have lit the fire – you must be freezing.'

Rose put on the light and some of the shadows in the scullery retreated to the corners.

Colin gave his mother a bear hug, almost lifting her off the floor. 'I didn't want you cooking all day, that's why, me old dear. Anyway – I've just eaten half a loaf.'

'Bet you haven't left any for me.' Rose kicked the floor with her new school shoes.

Colin rushed over to his sister and threw her up in the air. 'No, I didn't leave any for you, Dumbo, 'cause you're too little to eat – you're only good for eating!' He laughed manically and started gnawing at her leg.

'Get off!' shouted Rose, screaming with laughter. 'He's mad, Mum!' She broke away from him and ran around the room.

'No – just hungry!' He salivated noisily as he staggered around after her.

'Oh, stop it, you daft bugger,' Hilda said, shaking with laughter. 'I don't know where you get it from.'

'Dad, I expect.' Colin sat down abruptly. 'God, I'm tired. The journey seemed to take days.'

'I'll put on a nice cup of tea for us all. Rose – take your uniform off, there's a good girl.'

'Rose put your uniform on – Rose take your uniform off. Orders – orders – orders.' She stomped up the stairs.

Colin and Hilda smiled at each other.

'She doesn't get any easier, does she?' he said.

Hilda shook her head as she waited for the kettle to boil 'She's driving your Dad mad.'

'And how are you, Mum?'

They both listened to the old kitchen clock ticking in the silence.

'Oh, I'm coping … it's not –'

They heard the front door open and Kate walked quickly into the room, stopping abruptly when she saw her brother.

'Colin!' She threw herself at him. 'When did you arrive? Why didn't you tell us you were coming? Is Rob home too?'

'Bloody hell – it's like being attacked by a tidal wave – two hours ago – didn't have time and – yes.'

Kate registered the replies and gave a little scream. 'He's back!' Her eyes were brilliant in the dingy room.

Hilda wondered if she'd ever felt like that about Bill and quickly laid the table for tea.

'Tell us everything about the training, Col. It must have been wonderful,' Kate said.

Colin snorted loudly. 'Wonderful! Listen to the idealism of youth. It was bloody awful.'

'Idealism of youth! I'm not much younger than you.' Kate's eyes blazed.

'You're still in school.'

'So were you eighteen months ago.'

'A lot can happen in eighteen months.'

'Stop arguing you two and have some tea and cakes,' said Hilda, feeling very tired. 'No Viennese rolls, son, but I didn't know you was coming, did I?'

Colin looked at his Mother's tired face and put his large broad hand over her swollen red one. 'Sorry Mum – lovely to be back.'

Hilda smiled into his dear face, then looked at his uniform. Her heart missed a beat.

Bill stifled a yawn as Colin told them about the endless chores he'd had to endure so that he could get through initial training and into a squadron. He shivered at the thought of having to go out into the cold again for another Civil Defence Meeting.

They were all sitting in the scullery after having their supper. Bill had lit a small fire that was smoking badly as the coal wasn't high grade. They couldn't afford to heat another room now that coal was so scarce.

'I almost passed out in my medical,' Colin said, looking at his father.

'Oh yes,' Bill said automatically, stifling another yawn.

'The Medical Officer told me to blow into this tube and hold a mercury level on this mark for at least fifty seconds.' Colin drew an invisible mark in the air.

'What for?' interrupted Rose who was desperate for any information about life in the RAF.

'To test whether you'll be able to withstand pressure, Dumbo. I held it for ninety. Suddenly, the room was a black fog with red lights flashing on and off. Then I heard the Doc say "Pretty good – highest time so far, laddie. You can go." God knows how I found the door to get out.'

'Oh, yes,' Bill said, thinking of his bed.

'Daft if you ask me.' Hilda got up to clear the table.

'Then I had to stand on one leg with my eyes closed for a minute,' Colin continued.

'Why?' Rose asked, jumping up and standing on one leg.

'God knows – balance, I suppose.'

'Look,' Rose said. 'I could be in the RAF – I can stand on one leg for hours.' She screwed up her eyes.

Colin and Hilda smiled at each other.

'Don't be silly, Rose, you're only a little girl,' Hilda said.

'Oh, God! – it'll be all over before I'm old enough to join.'

'Rose!' Hilda snapped, not knowing if she was angry because Rose had blasphemed or because she wanted to go to war.

'What about Rob?' Kate asked.

'Rob?' Colin looked innocently at his sister as if he couldn't remember the name. 'Oh … Rob. He got the highest score for night vision.'

'Did he? So that's why he's so interested in the stars – he can see them better than –'

She was interrupted by a loud rat-tat-tat on the front door.

Bill looked annoyed. 'What time d'you call this to call?'

'8 o'clock,' piped up Rose, running to open the door.

Bill's face set in stone. 'She's too sharp to live that one.'

'Rob!' they heard Rose yell before he entered the room.

Only their shadows followed them along the sea shore as a full moon poured metallic brilliance onto the water. Rob and Kate watched the waves chopping it into pieces.

'The moon's the only thing they can't black out, can they?' She turned to see Rob staring at the stars. 'Rob?'

He was trying to pin-point the Milky Way. Millions of miles away from her.

'There've been more accidents in the black-out than there've been in the war, did you know?' Kate skimmed a pebble into the sea, trying to bring him back to earth. They heard its four quick hops over the water. 'Pretty good, eh?'

'Oh yes … watch this.' Rob bent down low to skim a small flat pebble. It bounced ten times across the sea. 'Got to get the angle under eight degrees.'

'Haven't changed, haven't you?' She smiled as she turned to look at his profile and was startled by the new angles in his cheekbones.

They scrunched along the shingle, listening to the suck of the sea.

'Mrs Humphries nearly broke her leg falling over some sandbags outside the post office last week.'

Rob burst out laughing. 'Searching for more German spies, was she?' He picked up another smooth blue stone and put it in the pocket of his greatcoat. 'Remember that day on the pier?'

Kate grinned as she thought of Mrs Humphries, their neighbour, whose face had the mottled look of a woman who had stood in too many queues through too many piercing, windy days. One day last summer they had seen her hiding behind the pavilion on St Leonards Pier, watching two men sketching the people on the beach. She had rushed over to Rob and Kate to tell them that the men were Nazis gathering material for a German invasion. Naturally, she told them, she was going to follow the spies and report the matter to the police.

Rob threw his arms around Kate, hugging her tight until they were both laughing.

'Oh, Rob – I've missed you so much. There's no one to laugh with any more.'

The laughter stopped abruptly. Rob tilted her face up towards his and saw how the moon had deepened the dimple in her chin; how it changed her blue eyes and long chestnut hair to almost black; the same colour as the sky. How different she looked.

'You've got your friends at school – your family.'

Kate stared at the moon casting long shadows across the wooden groins along the beach. 'No, I haven't.'

He cupped her face in his hands. 'What do you mean?'

She broke away from him and started walking towards the sucking sea.

'Do you believe in God?'

'What?'

'I think I believe in Jesus Christ, but I'm not sure about God.'

'What's brought this on suddenly?'

'It's not sudden … I'm trying to understand what's happening to me … I can't talk to anyone.' She crunched up and down the shingle. 'How can we believe in a God allowing war, Rob? It's not Christian to kill, is it? "Any man's death diminishes me because I am involved in Mankind."'

'You've been reading a lot.'

'Yet how can we let Hitler invade us … perhaps land here?' Kate pointed to the pebbles. 'I just don't understand anything any more.'

'Nor do I, but …' Rob looked up at the galaxy of stars that was spread out before them. 'Look up there, Kate, there has to be some purpose, doesn't there, when you look at them? There has to be some cosmic force outside ourselves that we don't understand.'

'But isn't that just superstition?' Kate looked from the stars to him.

'You could call it that, but there is a harmony between us and the universe. I can feel it.'

'You feel it, but other people don't. Men like Hitler don't. How can there be harmony in the world with men like him ruling it?'

'That's why I enlisted – to stop men like him.'

'But won't there always be Hitlers? Always men who are in love with power?'

'And won't there always be people like us who'll fight them?'

Rob stood behind her and put his arms around her. She leaned against the rough texture of his greatcoat.

'So we'll always have to fight … oh, Rob, I don't want to lose you.' He felt her shiver in the cold air and turned her round, opening his greatcoat to envelope her in its warmth.

'Come here, you, you're not going to.'

Her lips were soft and sensual and tasted of salt. He was always surprised by her kisses, so knowing, as if she'd been kissing men all her life.

She pulled abruptly away from him. 'How long have we got together?'

'A lifetime,' Rob said.

Chapter 7

'There were great numbers of young men who had never been in a war and were consequently far from unwilling to join in this one.'

Thucydides
5th century BC

The train didn't get into Chester until four o'clock. It was nearly five o'clock by the time Colin and Rob arrived at Hawarden Camp: tired, stiff and very hungry. They were depressed at the sight in front of them: the aerodrome was a sea of mud, littered with steam rollers and workmen who were desperately trying to finish the runway and dodge the planes that were constantly trying to take off and land. On the east side of the aerodrome they saw a black factory, which they discovered later, produced Wellington Bombers, flown by Vickers test pilots from the nearby Sealand aerodrome. So near, in fact, that a right-handed circuit had to be flown to cut down the risk of head-on collision with the test pilots. They watched the pilot of an old Hart Varient valiantly trying to take off in the waterlogged field, his wheels jamming in the mud.

'Christ,' Colin muttered.

Standing on the soggy grass in various stages of decrepitude were two ungainly Miles Masters Trainers, three old Tiger Moths and six elderly Hawker Harts with obvious patches on the fabric-covered wings. The Harts, they later discovered, also had poor forward vision when on the ground and their large fin and rudder area made taxiing downwind very hazardous.

'Christ – where's the bloody Spits?' Colin complained.

A tall, gawky man in his thirties ambled towards them, aware of what they were feeling. He had seen so many similar young men come and train in this aerodrome; many of them were still alive.

'Welcome to Hawarden. You'll be Pilot Officers Adams and Brazier. I'm Flight Instructor Dyce. Bad journey I expect.'

Colin and Rob dropped their kitbags hastily to salute. 'Yes, Sir.'

'Well, come over to the Dispersal Hut and meet the others.' He looked down at the mud soaking through the bottom of their kitbags. 'Watch out for that – it gets everywhere. Sergeant Rustum – Rusty – will show you your tent later.'

They looked at each other as they squelched their way to a small wooden hut. Their tent!

Twenty pairs of eyes turned towards them as they walked into the hut; their boots adding to the mess of mud around the door.

A tall man with an enormous ginger barley-eared moustache came towards them. 'Welcome to Hawarden, gentlemen. I'm Flight Commander Thomas. Some of this motley band of men will be training with you over the next few weeks. Flight Instructor Dyce will show you the ropes tomorrow. Must dash – frightfully busy.' Suddenly Rob and Colin were watching the retreating backs of the officers as they walked off, deep in conversation.

'Real home from home, isn't it?' Rob whispered.

'Where's the bloody food?' Colin was ravenous. He ran after the officers as they were disappearing out of the hut.

'Excuse me, Sirs, but would there possibly be any chance of some food? We haven't eaten anything since yesterday, you see.' The officers turned in surprise at Colin's interruption, then waved him in the direction of another hut in a corner of the field.

After a cold night spent in a bell tent with December winds howling through every crack, they had their first lecture in a packing crate that had once housed a Lockheed Hudson plane. It had a few windows cut into its sides and a tarpaulin sheet attached to its open end. Inside were a number of uncomfortable wooden chairs, a couple of tables and a stinking oil stove that emitted no heat. They were all sitting frozen at one end of the room facing Flight Instructor Dyce.

'And to think – we couldn't wait to join up,' Rob whispered to Colin.

'Good morning, gentlemen.' There were a number of tired, muffled replies. 'I'm aware that our surroundings are a little Spartan –'

'Spartan! I've seen hovels better than this place!' whispered someone behind Rob's back, his breath clouding with the cold.

'But the RAF hasn't time to indulge in the niceties of life – there's a war on, gentlemen,' Dyce said, looking at the young man sitting behind Rob. 'And it's vitally important we build up our air power after the fall of Poland. As you know, the Luftwaffe knocked out the Polish railway system and shot the Polish air force out of the sky. If Hitler gains control of the air, I don't have to tell you the consequences for Britain.'

Everyone shuffled uneasily at the thought of them.

'Air-Marshall Dowding wants an efficient RAF Fighter Command and I am going to do my best to give him just that. We have to train you quickly and effectively so I want your utmost concentration at all times. Over the next few months you will have lectures on aerial photography, air-to-ground Morse, artillery shoots, long-distance reconnaissance, identification of enemy planes, R.C. coding – in addition, of course, to tactical training in the art of aerial warfare.'

'Plenty of free time, then,' whispered Colin to Rob.

'You will be training in Miles Masters, Tiger Moths and Hawker Harts for Intermediate Training Wing and Hinds for Advanced Training Wing.' the Instructor continued.

There were a number of groans from the men.

'Yes, I know the Harts are old, but they're still useful old buses. You'll be divided into two squads and spend each day from 900 hours to 1900 hours alternating between lectures and flying. Any questions?'

Gradually over the weeks Colin and Rob got to know most of the men well. Les 'Chalky' White was a short, monosyllabic twenty-year-old who'd studied Law in London before joining up. He looked as if the sun had never touched him.

'How the hell did he pass the medical?' Colin had asked Rob when they had first seen him. He looked anaemic. But then as twenty-four-year-old Alan 'Stew' Granger, a self-confessed lady-killer said: 'They'll be letting monkeys with TB join soon.'

John 'Lightning' Lewis was nineteen and moved as little as possible when not flying. He was over 6 foot tall and lanky.

'Isn't it amazing?' Colin had whispered drunkenly to Rob one night after they'd watched 'Lightning' sit for hours without moving. 'Once upon a time that man was the fastest sperm in the race.'

Johnny Martin, with receding sandy hair, was the granddad of the course at thirty-two. He was married with one child and had a cigarette permanently glued to his lower lip: a mild man when sober, but when drunk, he had the habit of throwing glasses around. Then there was Harrison, an ex-accountant, very heavy-going. He spent most of the time reading books on the theory of flight in his hut and hardly spoke to them.

They were given codes that they learnt by heart. Chaos ruled in the local *Rose and Crown* at the end of one evening when Colin and Johnny Martin started their own private war by speaking into their beer glasses:

'Hallo, Dog-Rose Red Leader. Sapper Control calling. Are you receiving me? Over.'

'Hallo Sapper Control, Dog-Rose Red Leader calling. Receiving you loud and clear. Over.'

'Dog-Rose Red leader. Vector 120 degrees. Thirty plus bandits approaching Rose and Crown. Angels 10. Buster. Oranges sweet. No bumps or chickens. Over.'

'Hallo, Sapper Control. Dog-rose Red leader calling. Message received and understood. Tally Ho!'

They managed to smash most of the enemy glasses that the landlord had stacked neatly at the back of the bar before the rest of the squadron piled on top of them. Everyone from the camp was banned from the pub after that. Colin and Johnny couldn't remember why.

They progressed from the tent to a four-man hut in a corner of the aerodrome. At the end of a tiring day of lectures and flying, Chalky, Lightning, Rob and Colin lay on their beds obsessively asking each other questions about aircraft.

'What looks like a flying pencil? Has two radial engines and carries 2200 lbs of bombs?'

'Dornier Do17Z.'

'What's the fastest German bomber, similar to Dornier and carries the biggest bomb load?'

'Junkers Ju88.'

'What has a wing span of 74 feet, three 7.9 mm MG 15 guns in the nose and –'

'Heinkel He111.'

'What's the slowest British model, similar to the Michelin Man and carries 15 pints of beer?'

'Colin Brazier!'

The humour became more infantile as the course progressed.

'Right, start her up.'

Rob zipped up his heavy flying suit and buckled on his parachute, his breath coming in short gasps. He waddled out to the field carrying his gloves, helmet and goggles, towards the old two-seater Moth with Dyce following him. He had to convince him that he was ready to go solo on this flight or he was out of the squadron. He'd found out that he had a problem with his right foot; it was too heavy on the rudder – he had already damaged the wing of a stationary Moth by hitting it with his wing tip after landing awkwardly.

Rob walked round the machine checking all the controls for freedom of movement. He then climbed into the rear cockpit and fastened on his Sutton harness. Two ground crew held each wing to prevent the Moth from lurching forward when the engine caught.

The mechanic yelled 'Contact!'

'Contact!' Rob yelled back and swung the prop hard. He flicked the switches on as the engine caught. After warming the engine up, he ran it high to test the magnetos one by one. God – I must get this right, he thought.

Dyce climbed into the front cockpit. As he did up his harness, Rob noticed that Dyce's heavy flying suit had a fur-lined collar that was turned up, almost blocking his forward vision.

Do I tell him? He looked at the grim expression on Dyce's face and decided against it.

He taxied the Moth to take-off position that was just a section of the field outlined with small scrub evergreens, planted to give the pilots something by which to judge their altitude in an otherwise featureless landscape.

He could feel his hand hard-clenched on the control stick. Sweating. Ease it up. He forced himself to relax. The tail came up and with a slight bump, the Moth was off the ground.

'Climb up to a thousand feet and do a normal circuit. Watch your speed,' came Dyce's austere voice.

Rob straightened out at a thousand feet, fixed his eyes on the turn-and-bank indicator, pushed the rudder and stick together and gently banked to the left. Perfect.

'Straighten up and then bank forty-five degrees right.'

Rob relaxed back into his seat as he executed these manoeuvres. He was in perfect control. He did a few more manoeuvres before Dyce said, 'Okay – take us home.'

Already?

Rob flew back to the aerodrome and saw the strip of runway getting nearer.

'Don't forget the right hand circuit.'

He banked again, flying down-wind and changed into fine pitch, throttling back slowly. In the silence that followed Rob saw the ground rushing up to meet him too fast.

He was going to crash!

'Watch your speed!'

He pulled back on the stick.

'Don't overdo it, Adams!'

Rob's heart was beating too hard and too fast.

Christ – now he was going to overshoot!

'Hold her straight, man!' Dyce shouted.

Ease up with the right foot!

Then suddenly there was a slight bump, followed by another and they were down, droning along the narrow strip of field towards the men. He'd done it!

He felt his legs buckling as he climbed out of the plane, but forced himself to walk nonchalantly alongside Dyce who was humming quietly to himself.

'How was that, Sir?'

'You'll do, Adams.' And he walked off towards the Mess. 'You solo tomorrow,' he shouted back.

In the distance Rob saw the rest of the men shouting and waving at him and suddenly he felt the most enormous surge of joy.

They had all gone solo after twelve hours of instruction and were now ready to progress to Spitfires. Sergeant Rustum, Rusty, had taken them to the edge of the aerodrome where an old Spitfire was placed on trestles so that the wheels could be raised and lowered for demonstration.

'Good morning, gentlemen. You've lasted this long so the RAF must think you're good enough to fly a Spitfire. You've flown the Hart which is similar to the Spit, but there are a number of differences. As you can see, we have here a wonderful example of British technology – the Supermarine Spitfire Mark 1A. This plane, gentlemen, has a top speed of 362 mph.'

The young men gasped. They all knew that the fastest German fighter, the Messerschmitt 109 only reached 350 mph.

'The Spit has been designed as a fast-climbing interceptor to counter bomber formations, hence its rate of climb, 2,530 feet a minute, with a ceiling of 31,900 feet.'

'Bloody hell!' someone said.

'Couldn't have put it better myself, Sir,' Rusty said. 'On the right side of the cockpit, gentlemen, you'll see a large handle, about two ft long and beneath it, a smaller one.' They all stared as if mesmerised at the handles. 'This plane is not fitted with hydraulic brakes, so after you've taken-off, you have to lift the undercarriage handle out of the down position. Then pull it up as far as it will go, hold it there until the red light comes on and the wooden wing-indicators drop down out of sight. Then put it in the up position.' He demonstrated the procedure to the men before saying, 'Then you repeat the process in the reverse order to lower the wheels. Got it?'

They all nodded vigorously. Everyone was determined to agree with anything that Sergeant Rustum said.

They all moved closer to the plane.

'But – and this is important, gentlemen – don't pump the control stick at the same time or your take-off will look like the big dipper in Blackpool.' They roared with laughter – as if they would.

'You need to be a bloody genius to remember all this stuff,' Colin whispered to Rob.

Sergeant Rostum looked at Colin. 'Have I got your full attention, Sir?'

'You certainly have, Sergeant.'

'Good – then I'll continue. Taxiing – has to be slow because you can't see in front of you when you're in a Spit. So zigzag – then you can see … if you have a taxiing accident, gentlemen, you'll be fined five shillings.'

They all looked at each other. Five shillings was a fortune!

'If you get stuck in the mud, don't use too much throttle or you'll tip up on your nose and damage the propeller. Penalty is five shillings.'

'You'll have to cut out the booze altogether, Col,' Rob muttered almost without moving his lips. Colin looked at him, horrified.

'Get off the deck as soon as possible or the glycol engine coolant will boil,' the Sergeant continued, 'the penalty is –'

'Five shillings!' they all shouted.

'Good, you're learning fast, gentlemen. We don't have many accidents at Hawarden. Now here's the cockpit drill – RAFTS. R – retractable undercarriage – green light on, wing pegs showing; A – airscrew in fine pitch for take off; F – flaps up, wing indicators flush; T – trim – must be just a little behind the midpoint on the cockpit wheel; S – Sperry gyro in instrument panel 'caged' or locking. If there's nothing in the sky

– off you go – turning into the wind. That's all there is, gentlemen.'

'Piece of cake, Sarge,' Colin grinned at the Sergeant.

'Ah – the first volunteer.'

Colin's grin died as Rusty pointed to a Spitfire at the corner of the field. 'It's all yours, Sir … just remember … RAFTS.'

They all watched Colin take off at an awkward tail-down angle because of the mud. But he remembered the instructions Rusty had given about the drill and brakes. He grasped the pump handle and gave three pumps on the big lever, selected UP on the smaller lever and then pumped hard. He shot up in the air. He panicked, trying to remember what Rusty had said about the control stick and pumped it as well; the Spitfire started rising and falling like a roller coaster. They all watched this spectacle from the end of the aerodrome, roaring with laughter.

'And that, gentlemen, is a perfect demonstration of how not to fly a Spitfire,' said Sergeant Rustum wearily.

Rob couldn't wait for his first flight in a Spitfire. It came two days after Colin's debacle. He stepped onto the left wing root and entered the cockpit through the open hatch door and with some shifting positioned himself in the metal bucket seat moulded to accept the parachute pack. He moved the Sutton harness straps until they were positioned evenly over his shoulders and hips, holding him secure. Rob was six-foot and his body filled the cockpit completely, but he could turn his head readily without hitting the Plexiglas canopy. He checked the throttle and pitch-control quadrant mounted ahead of the hatch, with the turn tabs and radiator regulations immediately below. He moved the doughnut-shaped control column, surprised how easily it moved in every direction. On the circular grip of the control stick was the firing button. He checked that the firing button was in the *OFF* position. Directly in front of his eyes were the major flying control instruments; a complicated arrangement of glass and metal: airspeed indicator, artificial horizon, rate of climb indicator, altimeter directional gyro and turn and bank dial – all neatly centred, allowing him to look forward all the time. There were about fifty different knobs and switches that would be his constant guides in the future.

He switched on and a red circle and dot appeared like magic on the bullet-proof glass centre of the windshield, then gave the thumbs-up sign to the erk. The Merlin engine caught immediately with a cough and splutter and changed quickly into a quiet throbbing rumble as he throttled back. The machine vibrated slightly, seeming to come alive suddenly in response to the engine's power. He hooked up the oxygen tube and plugged in the radio cord after closing the hatch door, then signalled for the wheel chocks to be removed. Rob swung the nose from side to side to allow him to see enough to keep the aircraft on the taxi-strip without 'pranging' something.

He ran the engine up to test the magnetos, adjusted the seat to the lowest position because of his height and asked permission from flying control to take off. He gave a last quick check of brakes, trim, flaps, contacts and opened the throttle smoothly. The engine responded with a deep-throated roar and accelerated swiftly down the runway.

Christ how it accelerated.

Rob couldn't believe the power under his fingertips and laughed out loud. The Spitfire gathered speed with a pressure that forced his body hard against the contoured seat. The machine swung to the left and he remembered the problem with his right foot. He counteracted by increasing pressure on the left rudder pedal and sped across the runway – faster and faster – a short take-off and then the Spit freed itself from the ground at 100 mph. He moved the Wheels Up lever and pumped with his right hand to bring the wheels up into their storage space in the wings. He felt the nose rise and fall as he applied muscle to the pump handle. Within seconds the aircraft was clear and responding instantly to his lightest touch.

Christ – this was more exciting than sex!

Flight Instructor Dyce was watching him as he came in to land; flying downwind at 150 mph, cross wind at 120 mph. He lowered the undercarriage at 100 mph, dropped the flaps, only cutting the throttle when the Spit reached the line of evergreens. It floated down on all three points. A perfect landing.

Dyce walked over the machine just as Rob was climbing out, a huge lopsided grin on his face.

'Enjoy the flight, Adams?'

'Enjoy it, Sir! It was –' Rob looked around the aerodrome for words and shrugged his shoulders. Dyce, normally a serious man, laughed at the look of bliss on Rob's face.

'Well, don't get out – put her through her paces – don't forget the oxygen climb and dive-bombing,' Dyce said, casually walking back towards the dispersal hut.

Christ – I'm the first! The first!

Rob felt the blood pulsate through his body as he climbed up to 14,000 feet before attempting a slow roll. The Spitfire responded effortlessly. It was all the difference between driving a Rolls Royce and a Morris Minor, he thought, as he put her through every manoeuvre he'd been taught.

The oxygen climb.

He pulled back the stick sharply and the machine climbed to 28,000 feet. He blacked out for a few seconds and felt a momentary surge of panic, but the moment his vision cleared he relaxed and pushed the stick slowly forward to see the sun shining over the Irish Sea. He moved the gun button to the *ON* position and fired a few rounds from the Brownings. The noise in the enclosed cabin was muffled, but the recoil caused the Spitfire to momentarily drop her speed by 40 mph. He increased his speed and let out a great explosion of laughter.

Okay – dive-bombing next.

He jammed the stick forward in real dive-bombing style. The result was terrifying. The engine stopped running; a stream of petrol shot out of the vent pipe in front of the windshield and showered over the cockpit-hood. Rob shot up out of the seat to the full extent of his safety belt. A shower of mud and dirty water from the bottom of the cockpit hit him in the face.

Jesus Christ!

The Spitfire was diving steeply – the air screw milling round silently. He desperately closed the throttle and then opened it gently. Please God – work, he prayed, as the ground came rushing towards him. Suddenly the engine caught and started again. His hands were shaking as he brought her out of the dive. He had found the problem Dyce had wanted him to find – the Spitfire's Merlin engine, with a float chamber carburettor, tended to cut out under negative gravity.

Chapter 8

'It is one thing to show a man he is in error, and another to put him in possession of truth.'

Joseph Locke
An Essay Concerning Human Understanding, 1690

'I don't know what to say, Miss Brown. When did you see this happen?' Mary looked at Charlie's teacher in amazement. 'I can't believe it … Charlie has settled down so well during the last few months.'

Sara Brown looked at Mary, wondering if they were talking about the same child. She sat back in the chair and closed her eyes, utterly exhausted from having to teach such a large class. The evacuees had swollen it to forty-six children. She had very little equipment, and had to collect National Savings money, dinner-money and milk-money every day. Children like Charlie just wanted to run around the playground pretending to be pilots; dive-bombing any children who stood in their way. All the older boys' games involved fighting these days, she thought. She was heartily sick of seeing Bristol Blenheims, Defiants, Spitfires, Junkers and Heinkels decorate the walls of the classroom. There were other things to paint she repeatedly told the boys, but every Friday they painted more aircraft over the newspapers they were forced to use now as art paper. But Charlie's desire to fight couldn't just be attributed to the war.

Mary coughed and Sara opened her eyes quickly.

'Sorry – I'm really tired. Yesterday afternoon in Woolworths I was buying something for my mother when I saw Charlie with Rose Brazier. He whispered something to her – she looked very frightened. Then suddenly she grabbed one of those dolls in uniform they're selling now and they both rushed out of the shop together and ran down the road.'

Mary felt a pulse throb in her head and put a hand to her forehead. She suddenly realised where the little presents Charlie had been bringing her had come from. She thought he'd saved it from the pocket money John had been giving him each week.

'What shall we do, Mrs Adams? I haven't told anyone else. I thought that perhaps you could tell Mrs Brazier. I've so much work to do at the moment.'

'I'm sure you have.' Mary was trying to think quickly, but nothing would come. 'I really thought Charlie had settled. He's all right in school, isn't he?'

Sara chose her words carefully. 'Charlie finds it difficult to concentrate for any length of time when he does come to school, that is.'

Mary frowned. 'What do you mean – when he does come?'

'Well, you've been away for some time, haven't you?'

'We haven't been away for months … do you mean Charlie hasn't been coming to school?'

'I haven't seen Charlie for over two weeks.'

Mary was stunned. 'But he leaves the house every day to go to school.'

The women looked at each other in bewilderment.

Charlie was wandering along the sea front, looking for things on the beach. He had a collection of pebbles in his room now – all shapes and colours: light greys with blue traceries, blacks with large swirling patterns, browns with vermilion crescents, all exquisitely textured by the movement of the sea. He made patterns with them every night before he went to sleep.

He'd learned to sleep in a bed now, and found, after the first frightening night when he never expected to wake up, it was much better than the floor. He called Dr and Mrs Adams, Uncle John and Auntie Mary, and found it difficult to remember what his own house looked like. He missed his brothers, but he liked living with the Adams and loved the sea. He liked roaming, looking for things on the sea-shore, not sitting in a stuffy classroom, full of books. He hated school. He saw Rose racing towards him, her face bright red from running: she could hardly speak.

'I've just seen … Miss Brown coming out … of your house. You're for it, Charlie Slater … you are.'

'Oh fuck!' said Charlie, kicking the intricate pattern of stones he'd been arranging on the sand.

Rose gasped.

Charlie greeted John, who had just finished surgery, at the front door with tears streaming down his face.

'You ain't gonna send me away, are you?'

'What? Let me get in the house, Charlie.' John closed the door and stood in the hall looking down at Charlie's dirty tear-stained face. 'What on earth's the matter? … Come on – in the kitchen and dry your eyes.' He gave him a large white handkerchief to wipe his face as they walked. 'Now, where's Auntie Mary?'

'She had to go and see someone after the teacher come.'

'What teacher?' John sat down on one of the kitchen chairs and looked through the tall narrow window. He was exhausted as usual. The weeds had run riot in the garden, even growing on top of the Anderson shelter he'd built a couple of months ago. It looked like a brown igloo covered with that arc of earth, in spite of his efforts to disguise it by planting nasturtiums and marigolds. He rubbed his hands over his eyes. Another crowded afternoon surgery with problem, mounting on problem. The last thing he wanted was another one.

'Now sit down and tell me what's happened.'

'It weren't me fault – honest, Uncle John.'

John frowned. 'Just tell me, Charlie.'

So Charlie told John everything that he had and hadn't done over the past few weeks, watching John's face intently to see his reaction.

'I only nicked a coupla things – honest … and I hates school.'

There was a long silence in the room after Charlie had stopped talking.

'Why ain't you sayin' nothing? … Ain't you gonna hit me?'

John looked at Charlie in astonishment. 'Of course, I'm not going to hit you! Oh, Charlie…'

'What about a cuppa?' Charlie felt nervous as John continued staring at the garden. 'Why ain't you sayin' nothing?'

John suddenly looked at Charlie. 'Because… because I feel … very, very hurt, that's why.'

Charlie looked at him, amazed. 'Hurt? Where you hurting? You're a doctor – you can fix it.'

John shook his head as he put his hand over his heart. 'There, Charlie, there.' Charlie's eyes suddenly filled with tears.

'I'm sorry, Mum … don't … please … don't,' Rose hugged her mother tight as Hilda's large frame shook with silent tears. 'I'll never do it again. It was that *vaccie* that made me.'

Rose looked quickly at Mary who was sitting rigid with embarrassment in an uncomfortable chair in the Brazier's freezing dining room.

'How could you? How could you? Stealing. And don't you go blaming that lad. You could have always said no.'

Mary nodded at Rose. Vaccie indeed!

'It's come as a shock to both of us, Mrs Brazier.'

'I don't know what to think … you do your best, don't you? … try to bring them up honest … if her father ever found out.' Hilda gave a large shudder.

Rose's face crumpled. She looked wildly at Mary.

'You won't tell him, will you, Mrs Adams?'

'That's for your mother to decide, Rose, not me.'

The two women looked at each other. They had never spoken to each other a great deal, although Rob and Colin had been friends for years.

'No, I'll not tell him.' Hilda suddenly stood up, her face hardening. She held Rose's arms tightly as she sat her down on the chair. 'I'll not tell him, Rose, on two conditions.'

Rose shrank at the expression on her mother's face.

'What, Mum?'

'You don't ever, ever steal again and you stop cheeking your father. If you don't – I'll tell him and I won't defend you … whatever happens … agreed?'

Rose nodded her head quickly.

'Now up those stairs. I want to talk to Mrs Adams alone.'

Rose scampered out of the room and up the stairs in a flash.

'Mrs Adams –'

'Mary, please.'

'Well … Mary … I'll not beat about the bush … what are you going to do about Charlie? I'm not having our Rose playing with him any more after this – you understand, don't you? I've got to protect her.'

'He's not a monster, Mrs Brazier – he's had a difficult life. You can't expect him to change overnight.'

'I don't expect him to change overnight, but he's been with you a few months now, hasn't he? The other children haven't caused the problems Charlie has. Did you know he fights the boys every day when he goes to school? I don't like preaching, but he's an anti-social child. He needs some professional help.'

Mary stood up, feeling her face suddenly flush. 'Charlie's not like that in the house at all. He's helpful … he's bought me … John and I will talk to him, explain that he can't go about hitting children and stealing.'

Hilda shook her head dubiously. 'It's difficult enough bringing up your own children, Mary, but to try to bring up someone else's?'

John and Mary sat in the lounge drinking coffee. Charlie had laid a fire in there the previous evening and now it was trying to thaw through the arctic atmosphere in the room.

'What shall we do, John? It seems to be one problem after another with Charlie. I've got enough to worry about with Rob flying and all the other –'

She suddenly looked at the depression on John's face.

'Oh I'm sorry, darling – that was very self-centred. You've got far more problems than me.'

John took his glasses off and rubbed his eyes. They seemed to be permanently hurting these days. 'I don't know what to do, Mary and that's the truth. I have to be able to come back to some semblance of peace after the problems we're facing in the surgery. You can't imagine how many people complain of nervous disorders and I have to examine them all. I really don't want a multitude of problems waiting for me at home as well.' He smiled at her. 'I need my shining light to shine, my dear.'

She went over and kissed him. 'I'm sorry. Shall we send him home?'

There was a whimper outside the door. Mary opened it to find Charlie huddled on the cold floor in the hall.

'Why aren't you in bed? What are you doing there?' She brought him shivering into the room to sit near the fire.

'Couldn't sleep … you wanna send me back, don't you?'

'We don't want to, Charlie – you seem to be forcing us.'

A conker Charlie had put on the fire the day before suddenly exploded and everyone jumped.

'Why don't you like me?' His face looked pinched in the firelight.

'We do like you, Charlie,' John spoke rapidly. 'We don't like what you do. You go around hitting people, don't you? Good Lord – if I hit all the people I don't like, I wouldn't have many patients left. You have to find another way of dealing with people you don't like.'

'How?'

John looked at Mary in desperation.

'There's a lady at the WVS centre I work in, Charlie, who's very irritating. She sees German spies everywhere, which after a few hours becomes… difficult,' Mary said.

'What you do?'

'Well, we've all tried telling her she was wrong and she became very angry and started shouting a lot. It's very exhausting working with someone like that, so someone said, why don't we just agree with her.'

'What?'

'So in desperation we all did. Whenever she said she saw someone suspicious, we said we'd seen one too and she became very interested and started following them.'

John looked at Mary in astonishment. 'I don't know if I agree with that, Mary.'

'It worked, John. Mrs Humphries has become a very happy woman. She follows people around the town and leaves us to do our work.'

Charlie scratched his head. 'You sayin' I should tell kids there are Jerries in the playground? How's that gonna help?'

Mary smiled at Charlie's expression. He obviously thought her as mad as Mrs Humphries. 'No, you don't tell them that. You just agree with them if they call you names.'

'What? Agree with them if they call me vaccie?'

'Yes… See what happens.'

Charlie looked into the crackling fire and then suddenly looked up at John and Mary.

'If I does that – can I stay here?'

'What about the stealing, Charlie?' John asked.

'What about it?'

'You can't steal. It's against the law.'

'But what if they don't catch me?'

'Charlie – it's still wrong.'

'But what if I am not nickin' things for meself?'

'It doesn't matter who you're nick– stealing for, Charlie. It's still wrong.'

'Why? If we didn't have no food in the house, I nicked some. What's wrong with that?'

John felt exhausted, but knew he must try to make Charlie understand.

'All right, Charlie. I haven't any food so I steal some and then I'm not hungry.'

'Yeah – sounds good.'

'But what if I steal the food off someone who needs it more than me? That's not good, is it?'

'Well, then you gotta nick it off someone who ain't poor.'

John looked in despair at Mary.

'The law doesn't work like that, Charlie. It says you mustn't steal from anyone, however rich they are.'

'So a rich geezer could be stuffin' hisself and a poor one could be starvin' to death.'

'Yes.'

'Well, that ain't right, is it? Someone oughta change the law.'

'Oh dear, oh dear… I don't think I'm up to the task, Mary. I'm too tired.'

'I'll get you hot water bottle, Uncle John.' Charlie rushed off to the kitchen. They could hear him filling the kettle with water.

Mary went and put her arms around her husband.

'Oh Mary – what on earth are we to do with him, my dear?'

'We can't send him back to that poverty, John.'

'Then you're going to have to stop him stealing. I must go to bed.'

Mary waited in the room, staring into the fire, wondering what Rob was doing. She missed him so much. They had always talked late into the night about everything under the stars. She walked over to the window, shivering in the icy draught of air that whipped through the gaps in the ill-fitting frame and cut into her shoulders. A tapestry of winter lay before her, and above her – Sirius lighting up the sky. She remembered the night Rob had come bounding down the stairs to drag her up to his bedroom to look at Sirius through his new telescope: his excitement as he pointed it out to her.

'Can you see it, Mum? – It's the brightest star in the sky.'

Charlie opened the door quietly.

'Uncle John's gone to bed. He's clapped out.'

'Tired,' Mary said, automatically, moving away from the window to warm herself by the fire. 'Charlie, Charlie – what are we to do with you.'

'I dunno… let me stay here?'

'You saw how tired Uncle John was tonight?'

Charlie nodded. 'Works too hard, I think.'

Mary smiled. He was beginning to sound like her. 'He does … that's why he must have some quiet when he comes home.'

'He won't have no quiet if Hitler invades, will he?'

Mary shuddered. 'No, but he hasn't invaded yet, Charlie, and I want him to get as much rest as he can.'

'So does I.'

'Do you? … If you really do, Charlie. I must have a solemn promise from you that you'll never steal again. Not ever.'

Charlie screwed up his eyes and stared in the fire. 'I dunno.'

'What do you mean – you don't know? Why not?'

''Cos I dunno what *solemn* means.'

Chapter 9

'I said to the man who
stood at the gate of the year:
give me a light that I
may tread safely into the unknown.'

*From King George IV's
Christmas Speech, 1939*

Kate walked across the wide, nearly deserted, promenade of the Mall. She could see the trees bordering St James' Park, veiled in the grey-blue of late March; almost like a Monet painting. It was glorious to feel the breath of spring on her face after the freezing weather in January; the coldest weather on record. She remembered trying to battle through deep snow, prepared to walk to school, but had given up when she saw that the roads were impassable. It had been so cold one morning that when she'd opened the curtains, she saw birds frozen to branches.

Buds were bursting on the trees bordering the park. Her favourite season. Everything springing into life. It hardly seemed possible that Britain was at war. Then she saw the Regency facade of Carlton House Terrace, dilapidated by piles of damp sandbags, lying around its stonework.

She crossed Trafalgar Square, hardly daring to look across at the National Gallery she'd visited with her Aunt and Uncle as a child. All the pictures had been moved to a safe place in the heart of Wales, and now Myra Hess, the pianist, was playing in a series of shilling lunch-time concerts in one of the pictureless halls. People poured into the Gallery to hear her play Bach. The irony of war, Kate thought; a country soaking up the beauty of music written by a man whose nation they were fighting. She would have loved to hear her play Bach's *Preludes*, but she hadn't come up to London to listen to music. Below the National, a long queue of dark Lowry-like figures in their drab uniforms were strung out, waiting to get into the canteen they'd opened under the Gallery.

People bustled up and down the Strand, zigzagging across the pavement to avoid the sandbags piled in front of all the buildings. Their eyes looked strained. It was the waiting that depressed everyone more than the rationing of food and fuel, Kate thought. An unwieldy car swayed up the road at the statutory twenty mph, top-heavy with the gas bag on its roof, housed in a wooden crate. Many people had reverted back to petrol, although it was in short supply; at least a petrol-driven car didn't have a gas bag that draped itself down the sides and front of a vehicle when empty, looking like a deflated whale. Gas-powered cars had been a constant source of amusement for pedestrians for months.

She went into a chemist to see if she could buy some lipstick and cold cream. Of course, they had sold out. Behind the shop door was a large government poster showing two women sitting gossiping; Goebbels and Goering were sitting behind them, listening. It read: *Careless Talk Costs Lives.* Kate smiled as she opened the door – Mrs Humphries would be delighted – proof at last that spies were everywhere.

The WAAF clerk on duty at the Kingsway recruiting station didn't look up when Kate walked in. She just motioned to a door. Behind it stood forty other young women, standing against the walls, isolated by the silence and impersonality of the place. Their eyes darted towards her and quickly away.

A large, grim-faced sergeant, with deep lines chiselled in her face, shouted: 'Line up!'

The girls stood in an uneasy line as their identity cards were checked. An RAF Officer came into the room, looking distracted, and explained the oath of alliance at break-neck speed. Kate looked at the girls' faces and wondered if hers was as pale. Then he told them to wait for their FFIs. Everyone looked at each other. Kate walked over to the sergeant.

'Excuse me – what's an FFI?'

The sergeant's eyes swept up and down Kate's body before she answered impersonally. 'Free From Infection. You'll soon find out … in the next room.'

They were all ushered into a long, cold room with small, dirty windows near the ceiling. A naked bulb washed out any colour there might have been in the girls' faces. A number of medical orderlies were sitting at the end of the room, waiting to examine them. Kate felt her stomach contract.

'Right take your clothes off and line up in three lines,' shouted the sergeant.

A puny girl, who looked about fifteen, was standing in front of Kate. She started shaking.

Kate concentrated on the wall behind the medical orderlies' heads as she took off her clothes and stood naked, shivering with humiliation. Bodies, bottom-heavy from years of stodgy food, stood like animals waiting to be inspected; some were menstruating and holding sanitary towels or rags between their legs.

She watched each girl silently move forward to be inspected under the naked light until it was her turn.

'Bend your head.'

She felt her hair being parted with prying fingers, pulling at tangles.

'Arms up.'

She lifted her arms and one of the orderlies grunted when she saw her shaven arm-pits.

'Move forward.' Kate's head shot up as she felt fingers in her pubic hair, searching.

'All right – get dressed.'

Kate staggered back; the tears held tight behind her eyes.

Then she was outside the room with a shilling in her hands. A day's pay. She'd been told to go home and wait for papers that would inform her of her posting.

'You've done what?' Hilda's face was purple with anger. 'You haven't finished school yet! Have you gone mad? What will your father say? And who's going to pay the £5 for you to go before your Leaving Certificate?'

'I don't care what Dad says!' Kate's face was as angry as her mother's as she paced up and down her bedroom. 'I'll pay the £5! I'm not staying in school when the whole world's going up in flames. There could be another Guernica for all we know! You're always sneering that my head's stuck in a book – well it won't be soon. I'll be posted – somewhere far away and then you'll be glad.' Tears were threatening the anger in Kate's voice.

'Glad! – don't be ridiculous. You're only a child – you don't know anything about life. How do you know what it's like to have to fight?'

'How would you? You were serving tea to the gentry while men were being killed in the Battle of the Somme! Don't preach to me!'

Hilda moved quickly for a woman of her size and slapped Kate hard across her face. Kate's blue eyes glazed with shock before she ran out of the room. Hilda heard the front door slam. She sat down heavily on her daughter's bed, feeling physically sick.

Chapter 10

'This war, more than any
other war in history, is a woman's war.'

John G. Winant
US Ambassador to London, 1940

Kate arrived at Wolverhampton at 2.15 in the afternoon. She'd watched the green fields gradually disappear to be replaced by black chimney pots and grim rows of terraced houses. Another large sergeant, with a face like a hatchet, met them and marshalled them outside the station where a line of RAF coaches were waiting. Kate wondered if size was a prerequisite for becoming a sergeant in the WAAFs.

A small girl with a high pompadour hairstyle leaned over to Kate, tottering on black wedge-heeled shoes. 'I wonder what the bus service is like into town.'

'You'll have no time for sightseeing,' the Sergeant barked. 'You're all confined to camp for two weeks.'

There was a quickly suppressed wave of groans as the girls got on the coaches carrying various sizes of leather, linen and cardboard cases. Half an hour later, they stopped just inside the perimeter of a sterile-looking camp with rows and rows of Nissen huts and large hangers, surrounded by barbed wire.

'Lines of three. Quickly.' The girls were jostled into untidy lines and walked towards a group of oval-topped Nissen huts in a large anonymous field: all feeling self-conscious in their civilian clothes and high-heeled shoes.

Twenty of them were marshalled into a hut where a Corporal Smith was waiting to initiate them into camp life. She looked in silence at the hats they were wearing, covered with flowers and feathers.

'Right – get yourself a bed.'

There were twenty iron beds in two lines of ten pressed against the wall in the cold, impersonal, rectangular room. Everyone rushed to get a bed away from the door that had a two-inch gap at the bottom. An icy draught cut into their legs. Kate was too slow off the mark and ended up with a bed only a foot away from the door.

'Right – now listen carefully. One bed – iron.' She pointed, rather obviously Kate thought, to the beds. 'Iron lockers – hanging space for personal belongings.'

One of the girls ventured to open the door to one of the lockers and looked worried.

'If you've brought a lot of stuff – forget it – there's no room,' continued the Corporal. 'Post it back to Mum. On top of the beds are the biscuits.'

The girls looked at the beds. All they could see were three square mattresses on top of each other, covered by two grey blankets.

'They must be very small – I can't see one.'

Everyone looked around in amazement for the owner of the confident, educated voice. A tall girl with long blonde hair floating around her shoulders like the film star Veronica Lake looked from the beds to the corporal, tapping her foot. The corporal's eyes followed the noise. The girl's foot froze in mid-tap.

The only sound in the room for some time was the wind whistling round their legs as the corporal stared at the blonde girl.

'Don't try and be funny with me. The "biscuits" are mattresses. Each biscuit has to be placed on top of each other at the head of the bed every morning. Your blankets will then be folded to the exact size of the pillow and placed with it on top of the biscuits exactly as you see in front of you. Finally, the remaining blanket will be folded lengthways to the exact width of the pillow and wrapped round the original pile of bedding to form a neat parcel. Your parcel has to be aligned with every other bed on your side of the hut.'

The blonde girl raised her eyebrows at Kate in horror.

'The floor is covered with lino,' the corporal continued. They all looked down at the depressing, dark brown lino. 'It shines – that's the way it's going to be kept. Tomorrow you'll be each given a section to clean. It will be spotless every day.'

Kate listened with growing incredulity. The exhaustion was plain to see on everyone's face. They had been travelling for seven hours without any food.

'In the middle of the room,' the corporal turned to point, 'are two iron stoves. Tomorrow you'll be given a roster for black-leading them. Right – follow me. The cookhouse.'

It's like something out of *Tom Brown's School Days*, Kate thought.

They tried marching out after the rigid figure of the corporal. The cookhouse was a huge barn-like building with a mass of wooden bench-tables; so large that its corners disappeared beyond the dim lights. Another corporal was standing behind a table, waiting for them.

'Right – line up for your irons.' Everyone looked at the new corporal in confusion. Irons?

'Cutlery to civvies … guard these items with your life unless you want to starve.'

At the end of the table was a mountain of large china mugs that they discovered weighed a ton, even when empty.

'When you've collected your irons and mugs, line up for the food over there.' The corporal pointed to an area of the hall where cooks were waiting to ladle strange looking things out of huge pans.

Kate looked in disbelief as the cook ladled a brown greasy sludge with two lumps in it onto her plate. Her stomach rebelled.

After toying with the inedible food, they were marched to the Ablutions: six lavatories, six washbasins. No plugs. Two showers with duckboards and swing doors. Two baths housed in a corrugated iron shack. Kate noticed a foot gap between the walls and roof and shivered. On the door was a rota for booking them.

'No time for baths or showers. Lights out in twenty minutes,' shouted the corporal before marching off into the dark.

Kate lined up with the other girls to wash in a small sink under a naked light bulb. The water was freezing.

It was impossible to sleep on the hard, square, straw-stuffed biscuits that scratched her skin. She heard noises all night: the repetition of a grating cough, unsettling sporadic snores, stifled sobs. At last, a dim light announced the dawn. The cold soaked through the walls, up from the damp concrete floor, through the heavy, rough blankets that couldn't stop ice penetrating Kate's bones, making her shake as if she had scarlet fever. The warmth of Rob's arms seemed a lifetime away.

The distorted sounds of Reveille blared through the Tannoy at 6 a.m. The girls shot up trying to remember where they were. The nightmare of queuing for a basin in the cold the previous night was fresh in Kate's mind. She leapt out of bed, quickly putting on her blue dressing-gown and headed for the door.

'Bleedin' brass monkeys!' shouted a small dark-haired girl from Stepney, running past Kate to get to a shower first. The wind cut through them like a scythe.

The cookhouse stank of sweat, stale food and the cloying sweet tang of stewed tea. Kate looked at the glutinous mess of porridge in a deep pan and forced herself to eat it. A hard lump formed in her throat. She watched the other girls. None of them had made any effort to be friendly. But then, she thought, neither have I. The blonde girl came and sat down opposite her. 'Jesus – this is the second great mistake of my life.'

Kate looked at her. 'Second?'

'Yes … the first was getting married.'

A girl sitting near them, who looked as if she was made out of papier-mâché, choked on her porridge.

'You're married?'

The corporal marched in, shouting, 'Bed-making – five minutes!' and marched out. The news that the blonde girl had had experience with at least one man passed along the line of girls like a bush-fire as they hurried to wash their irons and mugs in a trough of hot greasy water and shook them dry.

Everyone tried to complete the complicated ritual of bed-making. It took them an hour before the corporal was satisfied. Each girl was then allocated a square of floor. Kate noted that the corporal gave the blonde girl, who was called Vanessa, the square immediately behind the door. Her red-lipsticked mouth hardened into a straight line as she looked at the corporal.

They all trooped to the front end of the hut where the NCO's bedroom was situated next to the broom-cupboard/cleaning room. The corporal pointed out the ancient irons sitting on a shelf, waiting to be heated on the stoves so that their uniforms had no creases. There were 'bumpers'; floor polishers which weighed a ton and had to be pushed back and forwards to get shine on their patch of floor.

Then they were marched to a large hanger at the end of the camp, trudging through mud. Some of the girls only had thin shoes, so by the time they arrived at the hanger their shoes and stockings were filthy.

Thank God, I haven't got the patch by the door, Kate thought, looking at the mud layering the hanger floor.

A number of WAAFs were waiting inside the hanger in a long line to issue them with clothing.

'Vital Statistics?' A WAAF asked a plump girl with neatly marcelled hair who was trying to clean the mud off the back of her stockings.

'Pardon?' she asked, blushing profusely.

The WAAFs looked at each other and sighed.

'Your measurements – you do know them?'

The girl blushed even more as she announced them in a quiet voice. She was given a chit with her size on.

'Give that to the sergeant over there.' The WAAF pointed to the hatchet-faced woman who had met them at the station the previous night.

'Next.'

They each moved up the line until they reached the sergeant who looked perfunctorily at the chit before shouting instructions to a number of corporals.

'One light blue cotton shirt, two hard collars – size 14. One black tie. One Air Force blue tunic – size 12. One air force blue skirt – size 14. Two pairs of grey lisle stockings. One pair of black Oxfords – size 4. Two pairs of blue rayon bloomers. One corset cover – size 36. One Air Force blue great-coat size 12. One packet of white tape.'

'Who wants STs?' the sergeant's voice boomed around the cavernous hanger. She waved a bundle of sanitary towels over her head.

A number of girls with very red faces put up their hands.

The girls staggered back to their hut carrying their pile of clothes, terrified that they were going to drop them in the mud.

The hut floor was caked with dirt by the time they had dropped their uniforms on their beds.

A thin girl in the bed next to Kate looked ready to cry as she tried on a skirt that was two sizes too large. Gradually they all discovered that the issue of correct sizes was a very arbitrary process in the Services.

'Friggin' hell – how can I march in this?'

Kate looked across the room at the girl from Stepney and couldn't stop laughing. She was hardly visible in her greatcoat; the collar nearly reached the top of her head, while the hem touched the muddy floor. Soon the room was full of hysterical laughter as they discovered hardly any of the uniforms were the right size. A rotund girl called Daisy, who had as many rolls as the Michelin man, had a skirt that only reached the middle of her vast thighs, while Midge, who looked like a stick insect, was wrestling with the standard WAAF bra, made of thick, coarse cotton with wide straps that completely covered her shoulders. It was bright pink. After five minutes of fighting with the hooks and eyes, the bra covered her entire torso. An auburn-haired beauty from Connemara, Bridget, started parading in an enormous pair of bloomers that she tied under her chin.

'Me Da always warned me to keep meself to meself but not as much as this, surely to God?'

They were lying helpless with laughter on the beds when the corporal walked in.

During the next few weeks, the girls learnt how to clean spotless floors until they were even more spotless by tying STs to the 'bumpers'; how to sew fifty-six pieces of white tape to their ill fitting uniforms; how to cram their surnames, initials and numbers they were given onto the tape with indelible ink; how to survive copious inoculations without fainting; how to survive the hated daily inspection without doing too many jankers; and how to march. They also discovered a tailor who charged them the extortionate amount of five shillings to alter their uniforms before they dared to be seen outside the camp for their first trip into the town.

The bus into Wolverhampton was overflowing with WAAFs singing:

My Bonny is stationed at ---
It's just as hush hush as can be
So nobody knows he's at ---
Except all his relations and me.
The gun he is guarding at ---
Stretches seventy feet in the air
And though you mayn't say you have seen it,
You --- well know that it's there.

Kate, Bridget, Tessa and Maggie had decided to go to the cinema to see the new film *Casablanca*. They stood in the queue with a crowd of Canadian servicemen and were repeatedly propositioned. Bridget turned her back on them all.

'Why can't I meet Humphrey Bogart walking down this street towards me wishing he could take me away from all this?' Bridget's arm swept around the queue.

'Because the Humphrey Bogarts of this world don't come to Wolverhampton, Bridget,' Kate said, turning her head away from a young Canadian officer with short, spiky, fair hair who was staring at her. She'd spent hours washing her deep chestnut hair in some cherished shampoo she'd saved. It shone in the late afternoon sun.

'Do you ladies want some escorts? It's kinda dark in there,' said the Canadian officer, pointing into the *Ritz* cinema as he smiled at Kate. He was surrounded by four other Canadians who pasted innocent smiles onto their faces as they stared at the girls.

'Indeed, we do not!' Bridget announced. 'What kind of girls do you take us for?' She swept past the men into the darkened auditorium, pulling Kate behind her. 'The cheek of these Canadians … Come on, girls.'

They reluctantly followed her into their seats.

'You speak for yourself, Bridget, in future,' whispered Maggie. She had seen a short Canadian boy with blue eyes that had smiled straight into her.

They glanced at her in surprise before immersing themselves in the film as the beautiful face of Ingrid Bergman appeared on the screen.

Two hours later, they were sitting rigidly in their seats as Bogart, misted in memories, made Bergman leave him for ever with her husband.

They watched as the plane's propellers twisted to the tune of *You Must Remember This*. Then Bergman and all the WAAFs in the cinema wept.

Suddenly, there was a loud explosion and everyone shot up from their seats. People started screaming. The cinema was being bombed. Pandemonium broke out as everyone ran for the exits, knocking over the manager who appeared in his evening suit, shouting, 'Don't panic! Don't panic!'

The girls looked for each other in the mêlée outside the cinema. Everyone checked for friends, then looked around to see the cause of the explosion. Suddenly, all eyes focused on Tessa: her uniform was in shreds – there was a large hole in her skirt and she was covered with wet, frothy, soapy water. People looked at her in horror. She'd obviously been hit – everybody else's uniform was intact. The girls rushed towards her and were almost knocked out by the powerful smell of peroxide.

'My God, Tessa – what's happened?' Kate asked her.

Tessa's face was the colour of a ripe damson plum.

'What is it?' Kate repeated.

Everyone stared at the hole in Tessa's skirt as she drew the girls around her like a shield.

'My peroxide's exploded,' she whispered. 'Oh God – I could die of embarrassment.'

'What peroxide?' they all asked her.

Tessa explained how she had rushed off to the chemist to buy some peroxide for her naturally blonde hair. When Bogart was making the greatest gesture of his life on screen, she'd been clutching a bottle of peroxide so tightly, it had exploded in her lap.

'Oh no! Holy Mary Mother of God – wait 'til the others in the Mess hear about this,' Bridget said, crying with laughter.

Tessa looked at her, horrified. 'You wouldn't?'

'Oh, wouldn't I, now?'

'She okay?' said the Canadian who'd smiled at Kate earlier. He looked concerned at the state of Tessa's clothes.

'Oh, she's grand,' said Bridget. 'It's just a small problem with her hair, she's got.'

The Canadians drove them back in an RAF truck after Bridget had calmed the cinema manager down by explaining about her friend who "wasn't really all there if you know what I mean". Once the manager had realised the problems the WAAFs had to endure by living in a hut with someone as unbalanced as Tessa, he had been most sympathetic.

'Is that what you call Irish blarney?' asked one of the Canadian officers, undressing Bridget with his eyes.

'And is that a problem you're having with your eyes?' answered Bridget, serene as silk.

The Canadians shook their hands and sucked in air, burning from her words.

The Canadian officer, Mike, who'd been staring at Kate, told her that he came from Ontario. Did she know that the word Ontario came from an Iroquois term meaning 'beautiful lake'? That it was about 1000 miles from east to west? That after the war, he would show her Niagara Falls, the most spectacular sight in the world? Kate laughed; she could feel herself coming alive for the first time since Rob had left her.

And on the other side of the swaying truck, Maggie was talking quietly to a young twenty-year-old Canadian who reminded Kate of her brother Colin: the same open, likeable face and ginger hair. His friends called him Banana Bob because his mother kept sending him bananas from Canada. And quiet Maggie was the only one who told the boy with the blue eyes that they were holding a dance in the Mess in two weeks and would all the Canadians like to go.

Chapter 11

'No profit grows where is no pleasure ta'en.'

William Shakespeare
The Taming of the Shrew

Sara looked up at the rain clouds forming in the square classroom window high above her head. She desperately hoped that it wouldn't rain again. They had a nature walk planned for that afternoon. Forty-two children, sitting in iron bench-desks in front of her, followed her gaze. Charlie was one of them.

'We're still going, ain't we, Miss?' Charlie, whose hair was now a shiny light brown, spoke for all the children. 'A bit of rain don't matter.'

Sara looked at their apprehensive faces, amazed at how they had grown; how fresh their skin looked; how healthy they'd become in six months. And how ironic, she thought; so many of them were better fed on wartime rations than they had been in peacetime.

She'd worked extremely hard over the months, teaching them to become confident with words and numbers; teaching the evacuees how to cope in a new environment; explaining to the boys that the street warfare they were used to in London wasn't acceptable or necessary here. Charlie had been the bête noir in her life until she had discovered he had the reading age of a five-year-old and could barely write a word. He'd managed to disguise this fact for months through his absences, until she had found him ripping up a book in frustration one day after school. She'd been horrified until she'd seen large tears in his hazel eyes. Why hadn't she spotted this earlier? She'd asked herself repeatedly, but how on earth was she supposed to cope with such numbers efficiently? Charlie had become the biggest challenge she'd had to face as a young teacher and she was determined to win him over. She had given up some of her precious free time to teach him after school two days a week. Charlie had sworn her to secrecy.

The children were still waiting for her answer. 'Yes, we'll go, Charlie... on one condition... You read out your work to us.'

Charlie put his hand in his pocket and clutched his precious stones.

The children all looked at Charlie and held their breath. He never read out loud. There was a long silence as he looked from Sara to his classmates; their eyes pleaded with him. He stood up slowly and cleared his mouth. The paper in his hand shook.

'The cow – the cow is a...'

There was long pause. The classroom clock ticked away the endless seconds as they waited.

'Mamal.'

Sara released the breath she didn't know she'd been holding.

'It has for sides ... rite left up and down ... at the bac its got a tail lik a ... lik a brush an wiv this tail ... it sends the flies away... so they do not fal in the mud an get dirti –'

There was a sudden burst of laughter and Charlie looked up, startled for a moment, until he saw the children weren't laughing at him, but with him. He gave Sara a small smile.

'– the head is for growin horns an so that the mouth can be somewere. The horns is to but wiv, and the mouth is to moo wiv. The cow is a nice mamal wot gives us milk.'

Charlie looked up, his eyes shining, as all the children cheered. 'We can go now, can't we Miss?'

Sara looked out of the window as the sun suddenly burst through a cloud. She felt like singing.

'Does any one know who wrote: "*Oh, to be in England now that spring is here*?"'

Charlie's hand shot up. 'Was it Hitler, Miss?'

'Oh, Charlie, Charlie.' Sara couldn't stop laughing. 'What a day for a walk.'

The children walked in a neat crocodile down the road until they saw the beach. Like young colts they raced over the sand towards the sea, shining like a green, glassy plain in spring light. All the rain clouds had disappeared.

Sara called out to them. 'Come and look in this pool.'

They ran over to Sara and gathered in a circle to look down into a miniature, lucent seascape. Multi-coloured seaweed curtains draped the sides of the pool, softening the textured shell gravel-bed. Sara knelt down and lifted up some small rocks. The children gasped as they saw plants, like sponges, clothing the underside; flower-like sea anemones with stinging tentacles, and barnacles, by the million, cemented to the rock surface.

'Ugh ... look at that thing in the seaweed, Miss – it's horrible.' Carole, a tiny girl who didn't like getting her hands dirty, was transfixed as she looked down at the seaweed. A small winkle, nestling among the weeds, poked its slimy antennae out of its brown shell.

Michael, a boy with a knotted thatch of hair, picked it up and tried to put it down the back of her dress. She screamed with shock and ran away.

'Put the winkle down, Michael, and stop teasing Carole,' Sara warned him. He reluctantly dropped the winkle back on the seaweed. 'It's all right, Carole, you can come back now – it's gone.' The small girl walked back to the other side of the circle, well away from Michael.

'Lift the seaweed up, Michael.' The boy looked at Sara, puzzled, as he turned over a large lump of seaweed. It was swarming with life.

'Crabs, Miss. Ain't they funny?'

They watched green shore-crabs trying to scuttle under the seaweed. Sara picked one up carefully.

'Look at them eyes, Miss.' The children's mouths opened in amazement as the crab's two bright eyes stared at them on stalks. 'Why they so high up?'

'So he can see if any enemies creep up on him. Look how his feelers work – just like a pair of scissors.' The children watched the crab cutting the air. 'He's lost some legs,' Sara said. 'Can you see? He should have ten.'

The children all peered at the crab desperately trying to escape from Sara's fingers.

'There's two missing,' said Carlos, a small Italian boy. 'Where's they gone, Miss?'

'Imagine being as small as him, Carlos, and living on the sea-shore with huge storm-waves crashing down and hurling rocks and stones at you.'

'Blimey – sounds like war,' Charlie said.

Sara looked at him. 'Yes, Charlie – it must be.' She put the creature back on the seaweed and they all laughed as he scuttled away.

'But there're other species of crab – look in the pool again.' The children peered for a long time into the water, but all they could see were shells lying at the bottom. Sara put her hand into the pool and brought out a whelk-shell.

'But where's the crab, Miss?'

She turned the shell over and inside its coiled entrance the children saw a hermit crab peeping out at them.

'Why's he live in a shell?' Carole asked her.

'It protects him, but it's not only his home, he sometimes shares it with an anemone and a ragworm.'

Carole moved back; she hated worms.

'Bit like us having to share our homes with vaccies, Miss,' said Michael looking at Charlie. Sara glanced quickly at Charlie and was amazed to see his expression hadn't changed at all.

'They all help each other, Michael. Deep inside the shell the ragworm scents the food and crawls towards the open end where the crab is feeding, then it creeps along the cheek of the crab and takes pieces of food from its mouth.'

'Ugh, that's horrid,' muttered Carole.

'Not at all. When the worm moves he circulates water through the shell and it helps the crab get rid of things he doesn't need.'

'Like a cleaner, Miss?' asked another girl.

'Yes – and the anemone does the same. It helps because whenever the crab walks, the anemone bends over, trails its tentacles in the sand and picks up the pieces of waste food. So they all help each other living inside this shell.'

Sara stood up and looked over to the ruins of Hastings Castle with a strange expression on her face. The children stared at her, puzzled. Suddenly, some of the boys ran off and started jumping on the bladder-wrack seaweed, hooting with laugher at the popping sounds it made.

'Boys, come here!' Sara shouted. 'Get your partners and start looking. Remember you get an extra mark if you see something first. You've all got your notebooks and pencils, so leave your shoes and socks here in case you slip in a rock pool and off you go.'

The children rushed to take off their shoes and, in pairs, ran over to the rocks that were clearly visible as the tide had gone out.

Sara watched them and smiled. They were learning so much from living near the sea. They could identify dog whelks and limpets and mussels; draw the differences between bladder-wrack and saw-wrack seaweed; identify different shells: the thin tellin in shades of pink, orange and white, the faroe blazoned with rays like the setting sun, the multi-hued banded wedge and the snail-like natica.

'Miss – Miss – we seen a sea anemone in that rock pool over there.' Two little girls with pigtails ran up to Sara excitedly. 'Come and see.'

Sara went over to the rock pool and saw the anemone's pink tentacles swaying in the water. 'And we seen it first.' They almost burst with pride as Sara gave them both an extra mark.

The children looked up as a huge mass of white birds with orange heads and long thin beaks swooped above the sea making *arrah arrah* noises.

'Sea-gulls, Miss,' said Michael, throwing himself down on the sand to write down his find in his notebook.

'No, they ain't – they're gannets, ain't they, Miss? – Rob told me.' Charlie looked quickly at Sara, desperate for an extra mark. She nodded at him. He grinned at Carlos, his partner. 'We spotted them first, didn't we, Miss?'

Ronnie, a large boy with a round, bland face and mousy hair, was Michael's partner. 'Naw you never – we seen them first – look, Miss I write it down.'

Sara inwardly groaned as she looked from Ronnie's notebook to Charlie's flushed face.

'But I said it first, Miss! – it ain't fair!' Charlie shouted in Ronnie's face.

Ronnie and Michael turned to face Charlie and Carlos; the four of them holding their gas mask boxes in front of them to use as missiles if necessary. Backs bristling.

'All right,' said Sara, quickly. 'How many gannets did you all see?' The four boys looked up at the birds swooping down over their heads and started counting. It was impossible because the flock was wheeling and diving all the time. The boys looked at each in desperation and pretended to count.

'Lots, Miss.'

'Forty-four, I'd say,' said Sara looking up at the birds in the blue sky. The boys nodded quickly. 'That's enough for all of you – so how many each?'

'Twelve, Miss,' Charlie and Ronnie answered together, with lightning speed.

'Good, so you can all write that you saw twelve gannets before the others, can't you? So you can all have extra marks.'

The boys grinned at each other before throwing themselves down in the sand to write in their notebooks. Sara took a deep breath as she walked over to the other children.

'Hey, Miss,' Charlie shouted, 'how d'you spell "gannet?"'

Sara suppressed a small smile of triumph. Four in one exercise: Natural History, Spelling and Maths. Not a bad afternoon's work.

Walking along the promenade back to the school, Charlie saw Rose and her mother on the other side of the street and waved. Rose waved back. She'd been to the dentist. Charlie knelt down, pretending to tie his shoelace so that Sara would walk past him. He'd spotted some flowers in a nearby flowerbed and leaned over to pick some bright yellow daffodils.

'See you tomorrow, Miss,' Charlie shouted after Sara, who watched him bounding across the road to where Rose was standing with her mother, his gas mask bouncing on his hip. She smiled when she saw the flowers.

Hilda looked down at Charlie. Charlie wasn't in awe of many people, but he certainly was of Hilda.

'Hello, Mrs Brazier – got something for you.'

'So I see, Charlie Slater. And where did you get them?'

Charlie's face coloured as he remembered Woolworths.

'I picked them from over there.' He pointed to the municipal flowerbeds.

'Those flowers are not to be picked.'

'But no one's gonna miss three, are they?'

'But what if everyone picked three, Charlie?'

Charlie looked around at the people walking along the sea front, oblivious to the flowers.

'But they ain't gonna, are they?'

'"He taht takes what isn't hisn, when he's caught will go to pris'n."'

'What?' Charlie looked up at her, confused. Hilda was talking a foreign language.

'An old Sussex saying, Charlie. Anyway, you're not arguing with me, are you?'

He looked at her, astonished. 'Naw – wouldn't dare – not after what Rose told me.'

Rose looked at him in horror. He went all hot and cold as he realised what he'd said.

'I mean … I don't mean … she just said … you were … you know … tough.'

'Tough?' Hilda leaned over at him. He tried shrinking into the pavement.

'I mean … you don't stand no messin' … that's what I mean – honest.' Charlie could feel sweat running down the back of his shirt in rivulets.

Hilda looked down at the agony on Charlie's face and suddenly laughed out loud. He looked up at her in amazement. He hadn't said anything funny.

'All right, Charlie.' Hilda took the crushed daffodils out of his tightly clenched fist. 'Thank you very much. Don't pick any more. Promise?'

'I gives you a solemn promise, Mrs Brazier – I'll never nick no more flowers from over there. How's that?'

'That'll do. Now what do you want?'

'What?' said Charlie looking innocent. 'Oh yeah …' He looked at Rose quickly to see if she'd forgiven him. 'D'you think Rose could go for a walk with me along the beach?'

Hilda looked from Charlie to Rose. She hadn't realised before how alike they were now that Charlie's face had filled out and he had grown: they were the same height; had the same shiny light-brown hair, although Rose's hair lay in two thick plaits down her back; the same sprinkle of freckles across their noses; the same need for speed. They could be brother and sister, she thought with surprise.

'All right, but no getting into mischief. Back for tea. Prompt, Rose.'

'Yes, Mum – bye.' She ran across the road with Charlie.

'Did you mean what you said about the flowers?' she asked him when they reached the sand.

'Course I did ... race you to the pier.' He shot ahead of her and called back. 'There's lots more flowers to pick, ain't there? I only said from over there. C'mon!'

They stood in front of the Hastings Pier holding their ribs, their lungs threatening to explode out of their chests.

'Blimey ... it's all that sittin' ... in desks what's ... doin' it,' Charlie wheezed.

They sat down against the black railings and looked across at the White Rock Pavilion, built in a Spanish Colonial style. A large colourful poster outside it advertised '*George Parker and his Band*'. Their chests gradually stopped hurting as they rested.

Above their heads, a canvas of vapour trails streaked the blue sky. Planes like miniscule flying fish were darting around each other, practising dogfights. Charlie leant his head against the railings to study them.

'That could be Rob up there. Wish I was with him.'

He watched a Spitfire roll effortlessly away from its opponent. 'I'm gonna be a fighter pilot like Rob when I grow up.'

They looked at the planes carving patterns in the sky for some time.

'What you want to be when you grow up, Rose?'

'Dunno ... I might be a nurse.'

'A nurse? – Leave it out! You ain't got no patience.'

'Oh yes I have, Charlie Slater and I'll hit you if you say I haven't.'

Charlie grinned at her. 'See what I mean.'

She punched him hard on the arm. 'Told you so.'

'Fuck – that hurt!' Charlie rubbed his arm. 'You're like a … wild mammal, you is!'

'"Are", not "is" and you shouldn't use words like … that.'

'Who says?'

'I says and my Mum.'

He looked at her quickly. 'Yeah, sorry about … you know. Your Mum's all right, ain't she?'

'Yeah – she's okay.'

They got up and crunched over the shingle on the beach while the waves swirled and sucked round the black iron girders of the pier.

Charlie suddenly spotted a large blue mottled stone and picked it up.

'Wow – look at that, Rosie … it sort of shines, don't it?'

Rose nodded. 'Charlie – why don't you want to see your Mum and Dad?'

Charlie looked at her quickly. 'Who says I don't?'

'Nobody … but you don't, do you?'

Charlie shaded his eyes and stared across at the pier. 'It looks like a giant insect with thousands of legs.'

Rose didn't answer.

'Look – there's some smashing pebbles over there.' He darted across to a nearby groin where a heap of pebbles had been thrown up by the sea. 'C'mon,' he shouted back at Rose. 'Ain't you gonna help? I want lots.'

'What for?'

'Gonna make a picture.'

They collected a mountain of pebbles as the sun advanced towards the west. At the horizon, the sea had turned to indigo in the changing light, moving into lines of emerald green nearer the shore. As Charlie created his picture the tide turned, advancing up the sand until the black rocks were all submerged. A large cloud suddenly obscured the sun, but the children were too engrossed to notice it or the gulls that formed black crosses over their heads.

'There – what you think?'

Charlie stood back and looked at the face formed by a multitude of intricately fitted pebbles with two dark blue mussel shells for eyebrows, two brown pebbled eyes, two seaweed plaits, outlined with small white pebbles, a rose-pink tellin shell nose and a cockle-shell mouth.

'Who is it?' Rose asked him.

'You, of course, stupid.'

Chapter 12

'Against infection and the hand of war'

William Shakespeare
Richard II

'I've been waitin' for years to find out about it,' Bridget said to the girls sitting near her. 'And it's taken a war and the WAAFs to tell me. I just hope the Virgin Mary isn't listening tonight, girls.'

They all grinned at her as they waited in the lecture hall for the officer to give them the long-awaited talk about sex. There were eighty girls in the room; the majority were only eighteen. They didn't have long to wait before the heavy tread of approaching sergeants was heard.

'Here it comes,' whispered Vanessa, who looked immaculate in a new uniform, even sitting cramped on a small hard seat in a stuffy hall. 'Don't blame me if you're disappointed, Kate.'

'You're the only one here who knows anything about it and you won't tell us,' Kate whispered back.

'Nothing much to tell, kid.'

At that moment, the officer walked in flanked by two hefty sergeants. The contrast made everyone in the room fight for breath. The officer was as spare and lean as a stork, appearing to have no breasts at all under her tight tunic. Her hair was pulled back tightly in an Eton crop.

'I wouldn't go near her in a shower,' Vanessa whispered to Kate who looked at her, puzzled.

The officer stood on one leg in the front of them, holding a swagger stick in her right hand. 'Now you've been here a few weeks, gals, I'm sure you've all settled in terribly well.'

Her plummy accent made a lot of them cough.

'What I am about to say may shock some of you having been brought up … delicately.'

Bridget's eyes were brilliant. 'Now don't listen, Mary,' she breathed quickly, making the sign of the cross.

'But life in the Services is not a delicate matter – gonorrhoea and syphilis are rife amongst servicemen. WAAFs, however, have the lowest ratings in V. D.'

There was a general stirring in the hall as everyone looked at each other.

'Bloody cheek,' said a girl sitting near Kate.

'And that's the way I intend it to stay.' There was a slight pause as the officer looked around at the girls. 'I can see from your faces that most of you have never heard these terms before, so I'll explain.' The officer paced up and down the lecture room on her stork-like legs, thinking about the best way to present these diseases to young girls.

'Sexually transmitted diseases have generally been a taboo subject for years, especially for women. Of course,' – she banged her swagger stick hard against her left hand, '– not for the men who transmit the diseases in the first place. Gonorrhoea and syphilis are both sexually transmitted diseases which can be avoided – if one never has sex with a man.' She paced up and down for some time before saying slowly, 'Perhaps I should say unprotected sex.' She looked up at the ceiling for inspiration before turning to the sergeants and nodding. They moved forward simultaneously as if a switch had been thrown and unveiled a blackboard that was covered with two large anatomical drawings of the male and female reproductive organs. All the girls, subconsciously, leaned forward.

'As you can see, gals – the male and female genital tracts.' She banged the board twice with her swagger stick. 99% of the girls' eyes widened in astonishment as they took in their first sight of male genitalia. 'Now … gonorrhoea is largely limited to the genitals – here and here – and urinary tract – here and here.' Everyone's eyes followed her stick from male to female. 'Symptoms appear from three to four days after exposure to an infected male. In the female the infection reaches the urethra – here – and birth canal – here.' She walked away from the board towards the girls. They all leaned back in their chairs. 'The symptoms may be so slight that you don't notice them – but be warned – in later stages you are liable to have major complications with your reproductive organs.'

Bridget's face turned very pale as the officer walked back to the board.

'However, gonorrhoea is as nothing compared to syphilis which starts in the female with a small ulcer called a chancre on the inside of the vagina.' A large number of girls looked at each other in confusion. The officer looked around the hall before pointing to the anatomical vagina on the board. There was an audible gasp in the hall. 'Next your lymph glands become enlarged – here and here.' She banged the board twice with her stick. 'But remember – this is only the primary stage. It gets worse.' A girl at the back of the hall fainted on the floor. Nobody moved.

'Unfortunately, the second stage mimics other diseases, so it is very difficult to diagnose. Common signs are rashes, painless swelling of the lymph glands, ulceration in the mouth, throat and around the genitals. This stage is highly infectious.'

Everyone coughed and shuffled in their seats, trying not to check various parts of their anatomies.

'This stage must not be ignored because the last stage – tertiary syphilis – is, I have to say, very unpleasant – general paralysis, derangement, degeneration of the heart, blindness and eventual death.' She paced up and down the hall before she nodded to the sergeants again. They moved forward like Siamese twins to uncover a number of photographs on the wall of syphilitic patients with sores and ulcers on their face and bodies.

There was a sudden audible intake of breath from eighty mouths and four more girls slumped to the floor.

The sergeants stared at the officer in alarm; many of the girls were exhibiting signs of shock.

'I can see that the talk has been effective, gals, so I'm sure none of you will be visiting our Medical Officer with such symptoms. It only remains for me to say that I hope you will all strive to fulfil the oath of allegiance you signed on joining the WAAFs, and do everything in your power to be an efficient fighting force for our great country. Thank you.'

She swept out of the hall with the two hefty Sergeants in tow while the girls sat in stunned silence.

Bridget was the first to speak. 'Holy Mary Mother of God – I can see now why the Virgin Mary was a Virgin.' She clutched the arm of the girl sitting at the side of her for support as she tried to stand up.

Kate's hut was littered with hair grips, cold cream, vanishing cream, lipstick, nail varnish, hair nets, dressing gowns, hand-knitted bed socks, pipe cleaners, hoarded perfumed soap and toilet water. They were determined, in spite of all the rules and regulations, to retain their bedtime rituals.

Midge was winding her thin hair round pipe cleaners because she'd lost all her valuable kirby grips.

Norma, a short, plump girl, was sitting up in bed, wearing the shapeless, striped pyjamas they'd all been issued with, encasing her neat marcel-waved hair in an iron helmet of kirby grips. Then she started on her face – plastering it with copious amounts of cold cream as she did every night, leaving two large circles around her eyes. They all wondered where she got her supplies of cream from. It was like gold dust. She hadn't told them her father was a chemist. She wiped her hands carefully before speaking.

'I think it's disgusting talking to us like that. I've never even been out with a boy before. I don't know what my mother would say.'

Kate stopped herself from looking at Bridget – they would scream with laughter: the thought of The Metal Panda with a boyfriend.

'Nor have I,' said Maggie looking more wispy than ever. Kate often heard her sobbing in her sleep at night, but she said she never remembered doing so. She brushed her short straight hair slowly. 'I wouldn't know what to do, anyway, even if one did ask me out.' Kate saw Maggie's thin, white legs dangling over the side of her bed, contrasting with the greyness of her dingy petticoat. Maggie always went to bed in her underwear as the rough WAAF pyjamas hurt her sensitive skin.

She was the sort of girl you wanted to hug, thought Kate: so childlike with her small, scrubbed face and under-developed body. If they hadn't seen her identity card, they wouldn't have believed she'd been born in 1922.

'Well, I would,' Jan said, the girl from Stepney. 'I've 'ad it up to 'ere with men,' she drew a line under her chin. 'Not worth the bleedin' time to get dolled up, I can tell you. Remember what Mae West said: "Give a man a free hand and he'll put it all over you." Too bleedin' right.'

'Well, really!' Norma put her hands over her ears. 'There are ladies present, you know.' Her mother would faint if she knew the type of people the war was forcing her to live with.

Jan looked at her as if she'd crawled under the door covered in slime. 'Oh, for Gawd's sake – grow up, you prissy tart!'

Everyone in the hut froze.

Bridget came in, wet from the shower, and took in the tension. 'Has someone died in here, recently? It's like me Uncle Patrick's funeral. Now come on, girls – what about that lecture then? Isn't it enough to put you off men for life and to think – me Da's one of them.'

They all laughed and the atmosphere instantly thawed.

Bridget bustled over to her bed in her pink padded dressing gown and threw some Ashes of Roses toilet water over herself. 'Now don't tell me I can't smell summer in this bottle.' She sniffed herself. 'It's worth every penny of 2/6d, so it is.' She lay back languidly on the bed in her striped pyjamas. 'Now then, Tessa Bingham. We've waited long enough. We want the truth about *Sex* and we want it now.'

They all turned expectantly towards Tessa.

Ten minutes later every girl in the hut, except Jan, had her mouth open.

'And that's supposed to be enjoyable, is it?' said Bridget. 'Well, I'll tell you something for nothing, girls – a virgin birth has my vote every time.' They all screamed with laughter before the lights suddenly went out.

Chapter 13

'Fear has many eyes
and can see things underground.'

Cervantes
Don Quixote,1605

Rob sat in the dispersal hut with the others, waiting for the telephone to ring as usual. He watched the men: some playing cards, others reading magazines. They had all worked hard at nonchalance over the months, but he could see a slight tremor in young PO Aerberhardt's fingers as he served the cards. Rob looked across at Colin, his leg swinging nonchalantly on one of the old hard chairs. He was telling everyone within earshot all about his old Mum's steak and kidney puddings, cooked in a rich succulent gravy and topped with the lightest of puff pastry. At any other time, the men would have welcomed a discussion of Hilda Brazier's gastronomic delights, but not before a scramble.

Rob returned to his letter, trying to concentrate on the words.

Hawarden 16th March 1940

Dearest Kate

I'm sorry that I haven't had time to write to you before but our training has been very tough. (Apart from the odd pint in the local pub drinking very watery beer that is. I met an old chap there who told me the government is diverting barley from the breweries to the bakeries. Is nothing sacred any more?)

Kate – why the hell did you join up? They're not conscripting women yet. You idiot – you were only a couple of months away from your Leaving Certificate. You could have been in University in a couple of months studying history, instead of living in a mud hut. (I know what it's like, so don't tell me it's fine.) Write and tell me what you are doing. I'm worried about you.

I've been posted to 616 Auxiliary Squad along with Colin and a few of the other nutters. Their enigmatic motto is 'Nulla Rosa Sine Spina'. `No rose without a thorn.' God knows what that means.

A lot of the officers here have sports cars – MGs, Wolseley Hornet, Le Mans Singers change hands at £20. Can't afford that, but I have bought a 1932 Morris Minor for £5. I just hope I have some time off to drive it.

The squadron has a motley collection of people: a lawyer who can quote every rule in the book, (and unfortunately does). A rake who thinks he's a stand-in for Clark Gable – (we've nicknamed him Gabs). Another fellow called 'Cocky' Dundas who is always planning some practical joke, an older chap called Teddy St Aubyn (I kid you not) is married to a girl whose mother, `Ma' Merrick, owns one of London's most notorious 'night-clubs', and a total eccentric Colin McFie, who never flies without a long, red tartan scarf round his neck.

I've clocked up over 200 hours in the Spits, Kate, flying my dream. It's so effortless that I feel totally invincible in the sky. I've been night flying – close to the stars. You know what that means to me. I've been a hair's breath away from Sirius. (Or that's what it felt like.) Can I bore you with the memory?

It was February; there was a light carpet of crisp snow on the ground. A dry wind rustled over the field as I crunched my way across to the Spit which was a dark patch in the night. I climbed into the cockpit feeling like Scott going to conquer Antarctica. I lined up with the Chance Light, got the all clear from the control tower, swung the Spit into the wind and I was away. Remember our conversation about God on the beach? I don't know what or who he is, but I was with some force that night. I was flying with the stars, Kate – not near, but with. It was the most mystical experience I have ever experienced.

After that flight, surrounded by the night, surrounded by the earth, I know that what Schiller wrote is true: 'Beauty is the product of harmony between the mind and the senses.' Kate – my senses were alive with the night; my mind was alive with the possibilities of what we can achieve. I think Byron was wrong about the image of eternity being in the sea – I could see and feel it in the sky.

I know I sound drunk, but I'm not, I'm 'in readiness' which means I have to be available to fly within five minutes. It sharpens the senses tremendously. I have never felt so alive in my life. Then suddenly – I'm with you on the beach listening to you quoting Donne and I think of what I am training to do – kill – and my body recoils at the thought. How on earth do I reconcile my love of flying with the knowledge that one day I will have to kill someone doing what he loves?

I have this recurring nightmare: my German friend Axel is flying a Messerschmitt in a clear, blue, summer sky – I'm flying towards him and I know I have to shoot him down. I'm flying nearer and nearer to him until I see his green eyes stare out at me through his goggles. I touch the gun button and wake up – every night – drenched in sweat.

I've stayed with his family in Bollensen for four summers, Kate and I like his parents. I know what makes Axel laugh. I know what makes him sad. I remember him saying to me once when I stayed with him in the summer of 1937: 'You know the trouble with us Germans, Robert – we search in the clouds for what lies at our feet.' Don't we British do the same?

I don't know when we'll meet, my dear love, but I know it will be precious.

I love you.

Rob.

He looked up suddenly to find the CO staring at him with an odd expression on his face and quickly scrunched the letter up in his pocket. Stretching expansively, he strolled out of the hut, walked around the corner and read the letter again. Then suddenly, he ripped it into tiny pieces and threw it to the wind.

Chapter 14

'There is a tide in the affairs of women
Which, taken at the flood,
leads – God knows where'

Bryon
Don Juan VI, 1818

The girls were all subdued as they listened to the news over the Tannoy as they were eating lunch in the cookhouse: Hitler had invaded Denmark and Norway.

'My God,' said Kate. 'Imagine what it must be like.'

They all shivered as they thought of Hitler invading their own country.

'I don't understand why he wants the countries,' said Maggie who didn't even know where Norway and Denmark were. Geography had always been her worst subject in school.

'I suppose so the German Navy can sweep down on British shipping in the North Atlantic,' said Tessa, whose father was a retired Naval Captain.

'They've learned from us from the last war,' Kate said. 'The Kaiser's Navy couldn't move an inch then.'

'Well, look at the mines we laid down.' Tessa's face registered disgust after eating a particularly gruesome lump of meat.

'It wasn't just mines – we had masses of war-ships patrolling the North Sea,' Kate reminded her.

The others looked at them in amazement.

'I don't know why you two don't become officers and win us the war,' Bridget chirped up. 'You're wasted here.'

'What – so we can terrify innocent recruits with tales of syphilis?' Tessa said.

'Do you mind,' Norma looked at Tessa with annoyance. 'I'm trying to eat my food. There's a time and a place for everything you know.'

Bridget looked at her plate. 'Oh, Holy Mary! – there's a bit of ulceration on me meat!'

They all looked down in horror at her plate before she burst out laughing. Norma got up and left.

'She's too nice to go the lavatory that one,' said Bridget, watching Norma delicately put her hands in the hot, greasy water to wash her irons.

A commotion at the other end of the cookhouse diverted their attention as the stork-like officer who'd given them the sex lecture swept through the room, flanked by the same hefty sergeants as before.

'She's coming this way,' hissed Bridget.

They heard the squeak of regulation shoes stop at their table and looked up to see the officer staring at Kate.

'Settling in well, gals?' she asked them.

'Yes, thank you, Ma'am,' Bridget answered in a demure voice.

'Good … good.'

There was a long awkward pause. The girls tried to eat the meat floating on their plates while the officer studied Kate.

'Food all right?' The sergeants looked at the officer in surprise. She'd never shown any interest in food before.

'Grand,' said Bridget, 'though I think I've heard the odd neigh, Ma'am.'

The girls choked at the puzzled expression on the officer's face.

Suddenly, the strident tones of Corporal Smith echoed round the cookhouse: 'Fire-fighting! Ten minutes! Quad!'

'That woman rations words as well as food,' Tessa said as the officer evaporated.

They finished their food at the double.

Eighty WAAFs stood at ease in the Quad: a concrete square where they practised square-bashing for hours every day. A robust Sergeant Benson was standing in front of an incendiary bomb with a lighted taper in her hand. She was flanked by Corporal Smith, who was armed with a bucket of sand.

'Right – I want your full attention,' shouted Sergeant Benson. She lit the bomb and moved back as it suddenly flared with an intense phosphorous light. Everyone gasped.

'Watch carefully.'

She turned to Corporal Smith who marched quickly towards the bomb with her bucket and tipped its contents around and over the bomb as if she'd been dealing with them all her life. The phosphorous flare petered out, leaving a trail of dark smoke in its place. Corporal Smith positively glowed while the smoke wafted out towards the girls.

'Pity she weren't sitting on it,' Jan said, blinking as the smoke hit her eyes.

'If you're efficient and well-trained, these bombs present few problems,' Sergeant Benson barked. 'However, we must expect the unexpected. What would you do if you saw a bomb lying on the road surrounded by oil?' She looked at them all intently.

'Run like a fart,' said Jan, leaning towards Midge 'Not much bomb disposal training in Stepney.'

The sergeant looked at her. 'That girl there.' Everyone froze. 'You – the one who hasn't got her cap on straight.' They all looked at Jan who insisted on wearing her cap at a different angle every day to accommodate her different hairstyles. Her face flooded with colour as the sergeant frowned at her. 'You've got a lot to say for yourself – you can help us with the next demonstration – follow me.'

Sergeant Benson and the corporal moved over to another section of the Quad. Jan looked around hopefully for someone to take her place.

'Don't waste time, Private Cotton,' the corporal shouted. 'Come on! And the rest of you.'

'Friggin' hell,' Jan muttered.

They all marched over to where the sergeant and corporal were standing. Another incendiary bomb was lying on the concrete surrounded by straw. At its side was a tin of paraffin, a stirrup pump and a bucket of water.

A look of horror flashed across Jan's face as Corporal Smith handed her the stirrup pump.

'You will now demonstrate how to use this pump, Private Cotton,' the sergeant told her.

Jan got hold of the stirrup pump, put it in the water and pumped hard. Her face became purple with her exertions. A short pause. Then suddenly a wave of laughter spurted along the lines of girls as rusty water shot over Corporal Smith's lisle stockings and black shoes.

'Your section obviously needs more training, Corporal Smith. The whole camp could burn down if the Hun dropped their bombs here!' Sergeant Benson frowned at the state of the corporal's feet.

Corporal Smith shot Jan a look of pure poison.

'Now let's do it properly. More water!' the sergeant shouted.

A number of corporals appeared from nowhere with buckets of water.

'Right – now watch.' She tipped the paraffin onto the straw around the bomb. Everyone tensed as she put the lighted taper dramatically over the bomb. Nothing happened. They all waited. There was a nervous titter of laughter.

'Ah, well – I told you to expect the unexpected.'

The girls tensed again as the sergeant walked casually over to the bomb with another lighted taper. Suddenly the air was full of phosphorus light. The next moment the straw caught fire. Soon the flames were ten foot high and black, acrid, smoke billowed around the Quad.

'Get the fire extinguishers! At the double!' shouted the sergeant over the whoosh of the flames.

Everyone ran desperately in all directions, away from the dense smoke that was choking up their lungs.

'Where the hell are they?' Tessa shouted out to Kate, her eyes streaming.

'Don't know but Corporal Smith will.'

'Gas masks on!' The corporal shouted at them, running to the Guard room to get the extinguishers. 'Then follow me!'

Within minutes the Quad was full of gas-masked faces fighting the fire with stirrup pumps, buckets of water and fire extinguishers. For once, everyone ignored the suffocating smell of heated rubber in their masks. Bridget and Maggie were holding a large extinguisher between them, determined to do their bit. The foam from the numerous fire-extinguishers cascaded over the incendiary bomb, cutting off the fire's oxygen supply. It died a sudden death.

The sergeant gave a signal to switch off the extinguishers. Everyone cheered as they tore off their gas masks; everyone, except Bridget and Maggie. The nozzle on the top of their extinguisher had jammed; a fountain of foam poured from it, Niagara-like, covering everyone in a coat of creamy white. It snaked in ever-widening patterns as they frantically struggled to switch it off. Soon everyone was sliding around, drunk with laughter, as the concrete disappeared completely. The sergeant and Corporal Smith looked at each other in consternation as the foam crept slowly up their legs.

Hours later, after they'd cleaned up the Quad and everyone had collapsed on their beds from exhaustion, Kate managed to steal off to the ablutions to read Rob's letter. It had lain unopened in her pocket for eight hours. She locked the bathroom door and sat on the edge of the bath.

Hawarden. March 18th 1940

Dearest Kate

I'm sorry I haven't had time to write to you before but our training has been tough. Hence the short note. Obviously something's in the offing, but I can't tell you what.

I was astonished to hear you'd joined up before taking your Leaving Certificate. Not a very good idea – you should have waited. But, of course, it's your decision, isn't it?

I've just found out that I have some leave coming up soon, so how about meeting up in London and then travelling down to the coast to see our parents together? You should be finishing IT soon, so can you drop me a line to tell me if this is okay?

Really tired, so I'll finish now.

Love Rob

PS. Colin sends his love too.

The letter fluttered to the floor as Kate covered her face with her hands.

When she got back to the hut she lay on her hard straw-stuffed mattress for hours with her eyes open. Why was Rob so cold? She suddenly found herself thinking about the Canadian Officer she had met two weeks ago. And not just thinking about him – wanting him. Did that mean that she didn't love Rob? She punched the hard rock of her pillow. The war was pushing her too fast into places she didn't want to go. She thought of the interview she'd had yesterday with the stork-like officer, telling her that she'd been singled out for officer training, along with Vanessa and Bridget. Kate and Bridget, unlike Vanessa, had declined the offer; they were determined not to fit into a mould of genteel conformity. The stork-like officer had definitely been displeased by Kate's refusal.

She got out of bed, listening to the heavy breathing all around her and picked her way carefully to the window, trying to avoid the tangle of uniforms everywhere. She pushed aside the ugly black-out curtains and opened the window. The faint sounds of Vivaldi, far in the distance, pierced the night. As she leant out, a large moth shuddered against the open window-pane before flying away into darkness.

She breathed in deeply. Newly cut grass. She had always loved the smell. And suddenly, she was lying on the grass in Alexandra Park in Hastings, late on a summer's evening with Rob. A twilight full of stillness. And then, in the trees, a sudden shrill call of a blackbird had sliced through the air. A thrush on another branch started singing an aria and soon blue-tits and sparrows joined to form a choir. Hopping and posturing, the little birds had sung out into the summer air. Rob and Kate had watched a tawny owl sweep out of an elm tree and a motley singing throng had pursued it. It flapped gracefully away through the trees and one by one the little birds had abandoned the chase.

It was only last summer that Rob had leaned over her, in the dusk of the park, to brush her hair from her cheek before he'd kissed her. She touched her lips and two large tears eclipsed her eyes. Looking up into the starry night, she clenched her hands on the window frame, trying to kill the questions circling her mind like mosquitoes.

Chapter 15

'This is a war of the unknown warriors.'

Winston Churchill. 1940

Hilda walked up Cambridge Road towards the Post Office, wondering how she was going to pay the rates. They still owed £2.10s out of the £5.5s bill, although she had been saving regularly over the year. Where was she going to find the money?

As she walked through the heavy dark brown doors she saw the Post Office was crowded as usual with women in their utility clothes sending parcels and letters to their husbands or sons. Long queues ribboned out in front of the seventy-two foot mahogany counter, guarded by an ornamental bronze grill, as if the authorities expected the Nazis to storm the Post Office at any moment. It must have cost a fortune to build, she thought. And a switchboard with 7,500 subscribers. Imagine.

She saw Mrs Humphries further up the queue and looked the other way. Hilda had too much to think about without more tales of spies. A play on the wireless called *I am a Jew* had upset her dreadfully. Hilda couldn't remember being so moved by a play before, especially when the little boy had said to his mother 'Will I always be a Jew, Mummy?' She caught her breath as she thought of his voice. It was the best bit of anti-Nazi propaganda she had ever heard.

She gave the lady at the counter the parcel she'd packed for Colin with some of her home-made cooking, aspirins and some insect powder she'd scoured the town for. She couldn't believe it when the woman asked for a shilling for postage. Just for a few items? Postage had gone up she was told. What hasn't? Hilda thought. She was just going to pay 10s into her savings account when she felt someone touch her shoulder lightly. She turned to see an old woman with unkempt hair and crumpled clothes; her sunken cheeks were highly rouged to disguise the pallor on her face and her lips had a blue tinge. She looked about seventy.

'Hello Hilda,' the woman smiled weakly and suddenly Hilda realised who she was. She tried to disguise her shock, but she could see from Doris's expression that she hadn't succeeded. Doris Hobson had been Hilda's neighbour for ten years before she'd moved to another area of the town. The last time Hilda had seen her she'd been wearing a smart, pale-green suit with matching gloves and a cream hat with a green feather in it. It was unbelievable. Doris was only fifty-five – three years older than herself.

'Doris – how are you?' An awkward pause. What a stupid thing to say, Hilda thought. She watched Doris' bony hands twisting and turning.

'This war's killing me, Hilda – my boys have gone overseas with the Army … and I don't know where … what am I to do?'

Hilda put her arm around Doris' shoulder. What a place to have such a conversation. With people listening. 'You're coming home with me, dear, to have a cup of tea. Bugger the rates.'

Hilda was up to her elbows in dough, feeling better for making some bread. Who was she to try to sort out the problems of the world? The platitudes had poured out of her when talking to Doris. How could you comfort a woman who had lost a husband in the last war and thought she was going to lose two sons in this? Join the WVS! Fancy telling her that!

Hilda pounded the bread with her fists. How was that going to help Doris get her sons back? How was it going to help her get Colin back? And suddenly Hilda's fists collapsed in mid-thump and she slumped onto the chair, sobbing her heart out.

Old Ribbon drip, old Ribbon drop
Cut him up in pieces and put him in the pot
Mix him up with ginger, mix him up with pop
Old Ribbon drip, old Ribbon drop

The girls chanted as they skipped on the pavement outside Rose's house.

Charlie suddenly ran around the corner and shouted. 'C'mon, Rose – you're supposed to be look-out!'

Rose dropped the rope she was holding and ran off after Charlie, leaving the girls standing with their mouths open.

Charlie, Michael and Ronnie were stealing milk bottles from the doors of houses on the West Hill Road.

'You've got enough!' Rose shouted. 'Come on – my Mum will kill me if she finds out.'

They all ran into St Leonards Gardens that was built for the Burton family at the turn of the century. It was set in a wooded valley and the remains of a quarry, surrounded by Gothic-style buildings. There were no strollers in the gardens that day, so no one saw the children go in.

'Right,' shouted Charlie. 'A long line over there.'

The children placed ten bottles in a line against the railings by the pond on which water-lilies lay in gold green circles.

'Got your bombs ready?' They all nodded as they got the large stones they'd been collecting for weeks out of their pockets.

'I go first 'cause I'm a flying officer,' said Charlie.

'You would be, wouldn't you?' Michael muttered.

'You wanna fight about it?' Charlie looked at him calmly.

Michael shook his head quickly. He had learned from experience that Charlie didn't play by any rules when he fought.

'Right then – ten in one. Nine in two. Eight in three and so on.'

They thought about this scoring system.

'What if I don't score 'til after ten tries?' Michael asked.

'Then you don't score, stupid.'

Charlie studied his target for a couple of minutes before lifting his missile.

'Get on with it!' Ronnie grumbled.

Charlie suddenly threw his stone in an arc until it dropped heavily on top of a milk bottle. Splinters of glass spun up into the sun.

'Yesirree! In one!' He danced an Indian war dance and shouted out a war cry.

'I thought you're supposed to be a British Officer, Charlie,' Rose said.

'Oh, yeah – forgot.' He stood up rigidly, before striding through the long grass with his arms behind his back. 'Mark that hit down for me, Corporal Brazier,' he said in a fair imitation of a public school voice.

'Mark it down yourself and why am I only a Corporal?'

''Cos you're only a girl, that's why,' sneered Michael.

'Oh am I? – well, this is only from a girl, Michael, so it won't hurt.'

She kicked him hard on his shin. He screamed in agony. 'You bitch! You ought to be put away – you're barkin' mad!'

'So you are, Snotface!' Rose yelled at him.

'Are we playin' or what?' Ronnie said, throwing his missile up in the air.

'I'm not! – I'm not playing with her!' They watched Michael limp through the grass before he turned to shout. 'I'll get you, Rose Brazier!'

'You just try, Snotface!' Charlie shouted back.

'C'mon – are we playin' or what?' Ronnie was bored by the irrelevance of the argument.

Charlie nodded, still looking at Michael's retreating back.

'Right – it's my turn.' Ronnie curled his fingers round his missile and threw it straight at the pond; it landed on a water-lily and sank ignominiously under the water.

'Bugger,' Ronnie whispered under his breath.

'Another go?' Charlie said, trying not to look triumphant.

Ronnie threw another stone, this time straight at a milk bottle; it disintegrated with a loud explosion of glass. The children cheered before they saw a large, flabby man trying to run across the grass towards them, his face puckered with anger.

'Hey – you bunch of vandals! – come here! – look what you've done!'

The three children tore up the park away from him. Charlie and Rose threw themselves into some dense bushes while Ronnie ran over the grass with the man puffing after him. They waited without breathing until the sounds died away. A rustle of oak leaves above their heads advertised the presence of two scarlet jays. The birds sat on a branch pulling acorns out of cups and gulping them down quickly. They flew off rapidly as a small grey squirrel scampered along the ground near the children's feet. It darted up the tree to look down at them quizzically. They both laughed as he disappeared into the leaves.

Charlie poked his head out of the bushes. 'C'mon – it's all clear.' They walked out, brushing leaves and grass off their clothes and sauntered past the pond, looking for all the world, like model children. They walked out of the park, past the large, white Masonic Hall with its entrance like a Greek Doric temple and ran swiftly across the road onto the beach, collapsing with laughter on the sand.

'Did you see that man's face?' Rose said, gasping for breath.

They lay on the sand, the sun streaming over them. Charlie suddenly turned over on his stomach and looked at the sea. It was very still in the sun, like a light blue skin. Two gannets were flying low in the middle distance, their shadows hazing the surface. He could just hear their faint cries.

'I wanna live here for ever and ever, Rosie.' He picked up some sand and watched it slip through his fingers. Rose rolled over, just as the gannets flew over their heads and disappeared behind some Burton buildings. She had lived all her life near the sea and had never really noticed it. She opened her mouth to speak, but shut it quickly when she saw the rapt expression on Charlie's face.

They suddenly became aware of the sound of workmen's voices behind them and stood up to find out what they were doing. All along the sea front, at regular intervals, Charlie and Rose could see they had dug holes in the ground.

'What they digging those for?'

'Dunno. Perhaps they're building something.'

'What – all along the beach?'

'Let's ask them.'

They walked over to the men who were dripping with sweat.

'What you digging all them holes for?'

'Well, he don't waste time in idle chit-chat, do he, Frank?' One of the workmen stopped digging to look at him.

'This is top secret this is, son – careless talk and all that.'

'How can it be top secret when everyone can see what you're doing?' Rose asked.

The workmen looked at each other. It had been a long morning.

'Look – will you kids push off – we've got to finish this lot before it gets dark.'

'Tell us what this lot is and we will.'

The workmen looked at each other again. Everyone was going to see it tomorrow anyway.

'We're going to put wooden posts up in them holes, and then tomorrow – you see all them lorries waiting over there –'

The children looked across the road to where a convoy of army lorries was parked. Where had they come from? Charlie thought.

'Tomorrow they gonna unroll hundreds of feet of barbed wire and nail it on our posts.'

Charlie and Rose looked at each other in confusion.

'What for?'

'Don't your Mum and Dad read the papers or listen to the wireless, son? To stop the bleeding Jerries from invading Hastings and St Leonards – that's what for.'

'But how can we go on the beach if it's got barbed wire all over it?' Rose asked him.

'You won't, love. Not from tomorrow.'

'What?' Charlie's face went white. 'But we always go on the beach.'

'Not any more you won't. Look – go home with your sister, son, and leave us to do our work.'

The hall at Christ Church was being used as a WVS Centre five mornings a week now. The long draughty room had three rickety trestle tables piled high with items to send to the troops: socks, soap, brilliantine, blankets, underwear, cigarettes, razor blades. Anything they could lay their hands on. Hilda had discovered a magpie talent for cajoling people into giving her items they had been hoarding for years; from woolly jumpers, Penguin Specials to unused toys; she was making a fortune in raffle sales. And she had an excuse to go out.

The women had been working for hours: some packing parcels; some unravelling woollen clothes; some knitting the newly balled wool into garments for their fighting forces.

'Tea and biscuits everyone?' Hilda shouted, trying to forget the pinched, tired faces of soldiers she had seen on the bus on her way to the centre. The acrid wave of sweat and damp khaki which had wafted around the hard wooden seats.

'Yes, please, Hilda,' shouted Doris who was so much better for having company each day. 'At least we don't have to boil up snow like we did when the pipes froze, remember? What a terrible winter, eh?'

'I love the winter,' said Alice Rodgers, a shy eighteen-year-old with fine, light-gold hair and a child's innocence. She was helping her mother at the WVS packing scarves for the Navy. Her twenty-one-year-old husband had gone to serve on HMS Hood. 'Remember me going to the West Hill with Dad, Mum, when I was little? Every winter he used to take me there and we made the biggest snowman in the world – a carrot nose and coal eyes. It was wonderful.' She smiled at the memory, then suddenly looked around to find every woman in the room staring at her. Alice's pale face flushed with colour.

Hilda was flying down a hill on a red toboggan with her father when she was six, laughing as the snow sprayed over her face. Doris was walking through winter trees in Alexandra Park, marvelling at the delicacy of fine patterns of snow on the branches. And old Mrs Bates, well over seventy, was snug in bed with her husband under an enormous weight of pink patterned eiderdown.

'I got six oranges for a shilling in the market,' said Mrs Rodgers, bringing them back to the practical. Alice's mother, a miniature 4 foot 8 inches, was always on the look-out for bargains, 'and I found some artificial crepe-de-chine for only 1/11 because it was soiled – marvellous for a blouse or petticoat slip for me and Alice.'

'How you can talk about trivialities when there's a war on?' said Mrs Humphries, who always wore the sort of heavy tweed skirt and long oatmeal cardigans that draped themselves over the stalls of church bazaars, but were never seen in shops. 'Don't you read the papers? Hitler has a Fifth Column in Britain – Fascists, Communists, Peace Fanatics, Alien Refugees – all in league with Berlin and Moscow. These people have been quietly infiltrating every organisation in Britain.' She looked around at the women's faces, wondering which one was a spy. 'They could even be in the WVS.' Her words dripped despondency into the room.

'You know they've brought in a new law, Mrs Humphries,' Hilda said briskly. 'Anyone caught spreading rumours likely to cause alarm could be fined £50.'

'Well, no one can accuse me of spreading rumours, Mrs Brazier. It's not in my nature.'

The women all bent over their work, suppressing smiles.

'I pray every night for Hitler to drop down dead, but God doesn't seem to listen to me.'

Hilda looked at her neighbour and thought if God wanted Hitler dead he wouldn't wait for a miserable old bag like Mrs Humphries to ask him.

Mrs Bates hobbled over to Hilda as she was making the tea. Her face, which had the dry, soft crumpled look of old age, hid the pain of rheumatism.

'I've got a couple of eggs here for Rose, Hilda,' the old woman whispered.

She had been keeping hens in her back garden for twenty years; dosing them up with whisky when they were poorly. No war was going to stop her. She'd showed Hilda what thrift really was one day by scattering bits of bread on her concrete garage floor, covering it with newspaper and running the garden roller over it. She mixed the bread with vegetable scraps and gave it to her hens. They gave her twelve eggs a week, she'd told Hilda. 'Isn't it appalling what people waste, dear – slices of buttered bread, half loaves, even small cakes?'

Hilda smiled at her. At least Rose wouldn't grow up on the poor diet she had had as a girl. 'You're right, Mrs Bates. When I see the waste in shop windows I think it's a pity there's no women like us in the War Cabinet … I'd like to have some of them come and stay,' said Hilda. 'I'd show them a thing or two and tell them what women thought – real everyday commonplace women like us who budget on a fixed income.'

Mrs Bates chuckled at the militant expression on Hilda's face. 'Oh my dear – I didn't know you were a suffragette.'

Hilda looked at her in surprise. 'Am I?'

Suddenly, Mrs Bates gasped with the sharp knife of rheumatism in her knee. Hilda looked at her in concern.

'Come over later, Mrs Bates – I'll make you a poultice of crushed chickweed – it's a wonderful sedative for rheumatism.'

The old woman looked at her, astonished: she had never told anyone about her ailment.

At that moment, Mary walked briskly into the room, apologising to everyone because she was late. She had been delegating more and more of the organisation of the WVS to Hilda. The Samaritan Centre she was helping to set up for homeless families was taking up an enormous amount of her time. She walked straight over to Hilda.

'Have you heard the latest news on the wireless?'

Hilda's heart missed a beat.

'No, not about the RAF … well – not directly.'

The women had an unspoken agreement not to discuss the news in front of Doris, whose sons were with the British Expeditionary Force in France. Doris managed each day by not listening to the wireless or reading the newspapers.

'The surrender of Belgium has created a vast gap between the British and French lines through which the Germans have poured. British and French troops have been driven back to the coast by a large German Force of 750,000 men; thousands of

refugees and troops have been killed trying to escape along the packed roads. A desperate rearguard action is being fought on the French coast around Dunkirk as German troops move in and surround them.'

'The first men of the BEF arrived home this morning after being picked up off the beaches, Hilda. I've just heard an infantryman telling a reporter that there were bodies of men strewn all along the beaches. Mass murder at its worst, he said … what on earth are we to say to poor Doris?'

Hilda's head felt full of broken glass. She went across to the sink and splashed water on her face and neck.

'Well, what's happened, Mrs Adams?' shouted Mrs Humphries. 'It's rude to whisper, you know.' She stood up suddenly. 'It's Dunkirk, isn't it? I told you, didn't I? – the army didn't have a chance against the Jerries. They're all finished, aren't they? And no RAF, I suppose.' She looked accusingly at Mary and Hilda.

The women all looked across at Doris, who'd been quietly sitting in a corner, knitting sweaters for her sons who were lying dead on the beach at Dunkirk. They watched her body slowly crumple on the floor; the knitting needles digging holes in the thick sweater she'd just finished.

Chapter 16

'Operation Dynamo'

RAF Code Name for the Evacuation of Dunkirk

Rob's squadron had been flying sorties over Dunkirk for weeks: sometimes two or three a day. He had stopped marvelling at the flotilla of vessels dotted in the English Channel, painting a festive picture; he had stopped seeing the broken bodies of men and vehicles along French roads and beaches; he had almost stopped seeing the ominous, dark clouds of smoke over Dunkirk spewing out pollution from bombed oil storage tanks. Each day, he had flown towards the thick column of ebony smoke, belching upwards until it cooled in the upper air to spread out in grey swirling spirals.

The squadron was flying at 27,000 ft, taking top position to protect the Hurricanes in attack. He looked around at the patchy sky, smoke caught up in layers of haze and cloud. France was down there, somewhere, under the translucent layer of dry mist. Down there, more troops were waiting for air cover on the beaches. He could feel the sun above him, but couldn't make out whether he was being burnt or frozen by its rays. Breathing was difficult at this altitude; he turned the oxygen on full to rouse himself. The strident roar of the engine increased the curious sensation of isolation he felt flying in a single-seater fighter. He was dreaming with his eyes open, lulled by the slow rhythmical rocking movement of Spitfires in echelon: by the gentle rotation of the propellers through the rarefied and numbing air. Everything seemed so unreal and remote. Was this war? Then he suddenly saw the yellow cliffs of the French coastline to the north of Dieppe.

'Look out, Yellow Leader. Three gaggles of 20 plus converging towards you, above!'

Burton's voice made Rob jump.

'Look out, Green two – smoke trails coming 2 o'clock.'

As Rob's eyes swivelled, he suddenly spotted the tell-tale condensation trails of German fighters beginning to converge on them from south and east.

Christ – they were coming fast! He released the safety catch on the guns.

'Red one calling. Keep your eyes open, chaps. Climb like hell!'

Rob opened his throttle and changed to fine pitch in the suddenly hostile sky.

'Prepare to break port – the bastards are right above!'

Two thousand feet above Rob's head a filigree pattern began to form. Suddenly, he saw the glint of the slender cross-shaped silhouettes of the German fighters.

Here they come! Rob's throat contracted and his toes curled tight in his boots.

'Yellow three, break starboard!' yelled the section leader.

Rob saw the roundels of Colin's Spitfire surge up before him. He banked his aircraft, using all his strength, opening the throttle wide, and rocked in Colin's slip-stream.

Where was the Hun? He turned desperately, glued to his seat by centrifugal force. Colin was weaving a hundred yards in front of him.

'Green two, attack port!'

'Yellow Two, break!'

Christ – that's me! With a furious kick on the rudder bar, Rob broke away, swallowing hard to stop the bile rising into his mouth. Red tracers danced past his windshield and suddenly he saw the bandits clearly – Focke-Wulf 190s – then everything merged into kaleidoscopic images: planes waggling wings; tracers criss-crossing; parachutes cascading like canopies in blue skies; grey trails from exhausts; white trails from wing-tips; black crosses; yellow bellies…

'Look out! – Jesus Christ! – Break!' A cacophony of cries in the earphones.

Chaos.

A Focke-Wulf, level with Rob, turned towards him. A quick half-roll, and without knowing how, Rob was on his back, finger on the firing button, shaking in the roar of the Brownings. He kept the Spitfire turning in tight circles. His finger convulsively pressing the firing button.

Beware, the Hun you haven't seen – he's the one who gets you. Rob felt the irregular thumping of his heart, hard in his stomach; the swamp of sweat in his groin as he desperately searched the sky. Where was he?

Then suddenly – a long way off – well out of range – Rob saw him. Quivering with rage, he fired futilely into the space where the Focke-Wulf had been as it disappeared unscathed into dense smoke.

Rob looked around. The sky was empty. He was completely alone. He felt like sobbing.

'Hello, Yellow Two. Yellow Three here – Where are you? Over.'

It was Colin's voice, a long way off.

'Hello, Yellow Three, Yellow Two here. Am okay – going home.'

Rob set course, 320 degrees for England. Five minutes later, his Spitfire was flying with one wing low at 200 mph. It needed all his strength to stop her rolling onto her back when he hit 350 mph. He flew to 25,000 feet and put her into a spin to see whether she came out or whether he needed a parachute. He shut the throttle, climbed until she began to judder as she stalled, then kicked the port rudder bar. Her nose dropped vertically and she began to spin crazily towards a rotating earth at high speed. He gave her a hard right rudder and put the nose even further down; gradually the rate of rotation began to decrease. When she was in a straight dive he eased back on the stick, pulled harder and regained some of the height he had lost.

Suddenly, the spire of Canterbury Cathedral slid under his wing-tip, just as his R/T burst into distorted life. A lone bandit was heading south from the area of Chatham. The Squadron Commander ordered a section to detach and go after it. Rob realised that he was in a much better position to make a swift interception than the section which had been detached. The Controller ordered anti-aircraft artillery to open fire on the bandit. Rob dimly saw the ack-ack shells explode in the area above Medway.

Don't be a bloody idiot, he told himself. Go home!

He broke the seals on the throttle quadrant to give him an emergency boost and his Spitfire shuddered under the strain. Suddenly, there was a dot in front of his eyes. The Bandit. He closed on it very fast, although his right wrist was almost breaking trying to keep the Spitfire in a level position against its left wing low tendency. In front of him was a Heinkel He 111.

Rob's right hand tugged at the control column, holding up the port wing as well as he could. He needed his right thumb to press the firing button – the left hand to move the throttle. He estimated the Heinkel was flying at 170 mph. The sweat broke over his body as he thought of his maladjusted aileron. He forced himself to breathe slowly.

Can't close in a dead astern at 200 mph. Okay – only one thing to do – head-on attack.

Rob flew past the Heinkel on his starboard side, keeping him in view by craning his neck until he was a couple of miles ahead of him. A steep turn to port, feeling the strain ease a little on his wrist; a tight turn to judge the distance between himself and the Heinkel; then he aligned his gun-sight. The Heinkel started to weave erratically as the pilot realized what Rob was doing, but Rob paralleled his every turn. His thumb stabbed on the firing button and he watched the tracers hit the twin engine bomber.

A hit!

He hauled back on the stick to pull the Spit up and out of the Heinkel's path.

Too late!

A 20 mm cannon shell hit his Merlin engine and flames licked from the exhaust tubes towards the cockpit. The Heinkel exploded – flying debris hit the Spitfire – oil burst across his windshield.

Christ – I can't see!

He looked down at the instrument panel; the glycol gauge indicated overheating; the oil pressure had dropped to nil. He had to get out – the flames were spreading. He had an image of burning flesh. Heaving the cockpit canopy open, he undid his safety harness, took a deep breath of oxygen, then removed his flying helmet and mask. He levelled the Spitfire, clambered onto the seat, and pushed the stick forward with his boot. Suddenly, he was hurled out of the cockpit by negative gee, spinning like a top in thin air, fumbling for the ripcord. He was moving through the air at about 200 mph and realised what might happen if the parachute brought him to a sudden halt – a broken back or unconsciousness through anoxia. He forced himself to wait until he felt the exhilaration that augured the arrival of anoxia and gave the ripcord a hefty pull. There was a back-breaking jerk as the great canopy flew open above him. Then he seemed to be stationary, high in the sky.

His Spitfire exploded 10,000 feet below into a million pieces of duralumin. He was drifting towards a wooded area full of ancient oaks and threw his arms across his face to shield his eyes as his body smashed into the foliage.

Chapter 17

`Who shows a child as he really is? Who sets him in his constellation and puts the measuring rod of distance in his hand?

Rainer Maria Rilke
The Books of Hours, 1905

Charlie was sorting out their collection in the garden with Rose. 'Look at that, Rosie – what y'think? – enough for a wing?'

They had been collecting pots and pans for the war effort for weeks and weeks. Rose had taught him how to persuade the women in the town into thinking they really wanted to give him all the aluminium they had. All the women, except Mrs Humphries, who'd threatened them both with her Home-Guard husband if they ever darkened her door again.

Mary watched them through the kitchen window, thinking how vigorous they looked with their tanned skin and freckles. Their light-brown hair glowed with health. Rose was chasing Charlie round the garden, threatening to hit him over the head with a saucepan; he was feigning terror. He'd obviously been teasing her again. Oh, to be young, Mary thought. She sighed as she took the chicken casserole out of the gas oven and put it into the hay box Charlie had made. It was going to save them a fortune in fuel he'd told her. She and John had never thought it would work, but it had. She was amazed at Charlie's ingenuity. In the corner of the kitchen were all the rows of buckets he had labelled: coal, coke, slack, peelings, fat, paper, wood. It was organised on military lines. He was the one who checked the blackout curtains every night to make sure the Jerrries couldn't see a glimmer of light; he was the one to scour the town for number eight torch batteries that were in short supply; he was the one who rushed to make Rob's breakfast every morning after he'd been released from hospital.

Rob woke up to find light slanting through his bedroom curtains, reflecting on his telescope lens, blinding him with refraction. He leaned over, then tensed automatically, expecting the pain to hit him. Hardly a twinge. A miraculous escape everyone had said in hospital. It hadn't felt like it at the time – every inch of his body had been in agony. He hadn't realised how excruciating extensive bruising could be. He'd woken up with an erection again – more sexual fantasies. If only he didn't love Kate. God, why was life so complicated?

He walked over to the mirror, pleased to see that the tincture of colours had almost faded from his face and body; there was only a faint trace of abrasions left. Then suddenly, without warning, images of the disfigured faces he'd seen in hospital flooded into his mind. Burned pilots. He flexed his left wrist, badly strained in the fall, and moved quickly to the window to open new visages. The heady smell of roses wafted up to him as he breathed deeply. In front of him was a silver sea; above him, a light haze. In his mind he could see the squadron flying in perfect V formations. What the hell was he doing at home? Churchill's words on the wireless the other night came to him: *"Upon us all the long night of barbarism will descend unless we conquer, as conquer we must, as conquer we shall."* Rob was desperate to be back in the cockpit of his Spitfire.

He heard shouting in the garden and looked down and smiled; Charlie and Rose were running round, brandishing saucepans, threatening to finish each other off. The transformation in the garden was amazing. His father had asked Charlie if he would like to 'Dig For Victory' and Charlie had taken him at his word. He had dug up all the lawn behind the Anderson shelter and planted every vegetable he could scrounge from their neighbours. They had potatoes, carrots, beans, onions, swedes, turnips, marrows and peas in profusion. Rob had never eaten so many vegetables in his life.

Suddenly, Charlie looked up and saw Rob; his face broke into a wide grin and he tore into the house.

Oh Lord. How on earth am I to tell him?

A few minutes later, Rob heard Charlie stomping up the stairs with his breakfast tray before bursting into the room.

'I cooked you scrambled eggs ... What y' think?' They both looked down at the mustard-coloured congealed lump on the plate. 'Yeah, I know, Rob, but what can you do with powdered eggs?'

'Don't use them?' Rob winced as Charlie plonked the tray on his legs.

'Yeah – I'll have a natter with Mrs Bates. She'll give me a couple of eggs for you. How's your wrist?'

'Great.' Rob had to remind himself to use both hands to eat now the sling was off.

'Lucky you didn't break it,' said Charlie looking out of the window.

'So you keep telling me.'

'Have you seen them?'

Rob moved the tray and walked over to the window. The haze had cleared and the sun was making a blue ribbon of the sea. He looked down into the garden at the four dustbins full of aluminium pots and pans.

'Saucepans into Spitfires, eh? – enough for three wings there, Charlie.'

Charlie looked up at him, puzzled. 'What? Planes only have two.'

Rob smiled. 'Know what we're going to do today?'

'Not 'til you tell me.'

'We're going to get Kate and Rose and go for a walk along the front.'

'But we can't! – not with the barbed wire!' Charlie's face flushed with anger.

'Hey – we can still walk along the promenade and then we're going to see a Heinkel.'

'A Heinkel? Where?' Charlie yelled.

'You'll see ... now take that disgusting yellow lump away and let me get dressed.'

Rob and Kate were walking hand in hand along the promenade past the Palace Pier: an incongruous mix of Victorian architecture and American-style lighting. Thank God the large neon lighting strip that shouted *DANCING* had been switched off since the black-out, Rob thought. The white arches at the entrance looked like some scenery from a film set. He could see the empty bandstand where he'd listened to a small orchestra playing a Strauss waltz. He'd been twelve, eating an enormous creamy ice cream and his father had been tapping out Strauss' rhythms with his foot.

'My God – look what they've done to the town, Kate.'

All along the coast, as far as the eye could see, were tank traps: two lines of rectangular blocks of solid concrete, paralleled, but staggered in such a way that they would prevent entry from amphibious landing craft. They had already been nicknamed 'dragon's teeth'. On the East and West Hills were ugly concrete pillboxes, but worst of all, he thought, were the barbed wire entanglements.

A poem surfaced as he looked at the disfigurement of the barbed wire:

Thorns rust the shore with crosses
War stamps the sun of light
The flowers have no faces

And day has met with night.

Kate looked at him, wanting his mood to lighten.

'Look – they've still got the name-punching machines on the pier.'

'Good God – so they have … Charlie! Rose!' Rob shouted to the children who were running ahead as usual. He waved them back. 'Come here!'

They raced towards him, their long, thin legs flying behind them, almost knocking Rob and Kate over.

'Whoa! – slow down. We want to show you something.'

They herded the children towards the machines by the black iron railings.

'Who's first?'

Charlie's arm shot up. 'Me.'

Rob gave him a farthing and showed him how to punch out his name on the metal tape. They all watched as he punched out CHARLIE.

'My turn.' Rose was hopping from foot to foot with impatience. She punched ROSE BRAZIER into the metal. 'Look, Charlie … You forgot your surname.'

Charlie turned away from her to look at the sea. 'No, I didn't.'

There was a small silence before Charlie raced back up the pier onto the promenade. 'C'mon. I want to see the Heinkel.'

Rose raced off after him. They watched them disappearing into the distance.

'Did we ever have that much energy, Kate?'

'Course we did,' she said, smiling at him. 'I still have.'

He smiled back at her. 'I feel so light without my flying suit. I could almost float away.' He looked down at the unfamiliar navy slacks and white short-sleeved shirt he was wearing.

'You might – you're too thin,' said Kate. They had only just fallen back into their old relationship. Kate's one visit to the hospital had been sterile. A bruised stranger had lain in a bed, emotionally out of reach and she hadn't known why.

She smiled at him again, looking radiant. The sun made a halo around her chestnut hair and her skin was so translucent it looked as if it had been lit from inside. Rob could see himself mirrored endlessly in the ultramarine of her eyes. He forced himself to look away.

On the other side of the road was *D'Marcos*, the Italian restaurant his parents had taken him to after he'd passed his Matriculation; boarded up now and the owners interned on the Isle of Man. He remembered Charlie bringing Carlos, the owner's son, home for tea before the family had had to leave. The anger on Charlie's face when he had tried to explain why they had been interned.

Suddenly, he felt Kate pull his hand and became aware of a commotion in the distance. They could see Charlie and Rose standing in a crowd of milling people by the Hastings Pier. Something was wrong. They started to run. Kate was way ahead of Rob within seconds, fit from her training, whereas he was weak from lying in bed. By the time he reached Kate, the crowd was shouting at two haggard, sea-soaked, coal-begrimed men, standing on board a small steam tug at the side of the pier, carrying suitcases. People were igniting each other with words.

'Bloody Nazis!' 'Where's the police?' 'Shoot 'em I say!' 'Fuckin' nerve turning up here!' 'Let's get them!' 'String 'em up!'

The men on the tug looked terrified. Suddenly one of them burst out with a stream of French.

'On travaille pour les chemins de fer belges et on s'est échappé avec la paie de treize millions de francs!' The man waved a suitcase at the crowd. 'Y'avait plus de bateaux dans les ports belges, mais on a trouvé un remorqueur et on est parti vers l'Angleterre - sans compas - on s'est juste arrêté à un phare pour demander le chemin.'

This silenced the crowd for a minute until someone shouted.

'Now they're pretending to be French! The Bastards!'

Some men in the crowd started to climb down the railings towards the tug, while the coal-streaked men shouted at the top of their voices. 'On peut prouver ce qu'on dit – si seulement vous regardez dans nos valises!' over and over again.

Suddenly Rob bellowed. 'For God's sake – they might be refugees!'

The crowd looked from Rob to the men who were still shouting and holding up their suitcases.

'Yeah – they might be refugees!' Charlie shouted, adding to the mayhem.

Astonishment was written all over the faces of people who could understand French.

'What they saying?' shouted a heavyweight man with a battered face who looked as if boxing was his only hobby.

'They work for the Belgium Railways. They've got the payroll – 13,000,000 francs in those suitcases,' Rob shouted out. 'Unbelievable.'

'One way to prove it, mate. Tell 'em to open the cases.'

Charlie crept up to Rob and whispered, 'What's a refugee?'

The men on the steam tub suddenly remembered their English and opened the suitcases before Rob could speak. There, in front of the crowd, were thousands and thousands of Belgium bank notes. Everyone gasped.

'Well, I'll be buggered,' said the battered-looking man.

Two hours later, the crowd had dispersed and the police had taken the men away for questioning. Later, '*The Hastings and St Leonards Observer*' printed the whole incredible story. One of the men was the financial director of the Belgian State

Railway; the other was the Chief Engineer. After Belgium had fallen to the Germans, they had tried to escape with the payroll so it wouldn't fall into Nazi hands, but found that all the ships had left the Belgian ports with refugees on board. The only boat left was a small steam tug with no compass or charts. Without any experience of piloting boats they had managed to steam across the channel, taking turns to sleep in the stoke hole, the only place that was warm on the boat, hence their filthy appearance. The Director said that Providence must have guided them to Hastings.

'Blimey,' said Charlie.

'And I thought coming home would be quiet,' said Rob, feeling incredibly tired.

Kate looked at his drawn features. 'We ought to go home.'

'But what about the Heinkel, Rob?' Charlie was desperate.

'We can see the Heinkel any time,' said Rose aggressively.

'How d'you know?'

'Because I read the papers. It's on show at Summerfields for weeks. They're trying to raise money for the Spitfire Fund. Don't you know anything?'

Rob looked at Charlie's face and could have throttled Rose.

'We'll go tomorrow, Charlie. I promise,' Rob told him.

'All right,' said Charlie flatly and walked off down the promenade by himself.

Kate shook her head as she looked down at her sister. 'Why can't you ever learn to shut up, Rose. You can be so nasty.'

Rose's mouth twitched; suddenly tears were pouring down her face. Kate crouched down beside her.

'What's the matter?'

'It's the newspaper, she sobbed, 'the evacuees ...'

Kate looked up at Rob in alarm, suddenly recalling the article they had both read that morning:

"Since Hastings has ceased to be a safe reception area after the fall of France, the Evacuation Committee has organised the removal of all London evacuees from Hastings to South Wales within the next two weeks. So far, there are no plans to evacuate local children. However, all parents or guardians will be notified immediately of any change in these arrangements."

'Oh God,' said Rob. 'I'll have to tell him tonight.'

Chapter 18

'Everything is determined; the beginning as well as the end, by forces over which we have no control ... We all dance to an invisible tune intoned in the distance by an invisible piper.'

Einstein
Saturday Evening Post. 26th October, 1929

The sky was a dusky blue, not yet sunk into the bluish-black of night. One or two pin-point stars were visible beyond the light of Venus. Rob looked out to sea. Yellow replicas rocked on its surface. Charlie was looking through Rob's telescope.

'I can't see it, Rob.'

'Look higher.' Rob pointed out Venus to him. 'It's the most brilliant of the planets.'

'I got it!' Charlie shouted in excitement. 'Blimey! It's big!'

'It's sixty-seven million miles from the Sun. It's called the Morning Star when it appears in the east at sunrise, and the Evening Star when it's in the west at sunset ... Now look twenty degrees to your left, Charlie, and you'll see Mars – fourth planet from the Sun.'

Charlie moved the angle of the telescope. 'It's red!'

'That's why they called it Mars, after the Roman God of war.'

'D'you think there's men on it?'

'I don't think so – not men like us anyway. It has hardly any gravity and the temperature's minus sixty degrees centigrade.'

'What's gravity?' Charlie asked, looking up at Rob, his eyes wide with wonder at the night sky.

An incredible sadness washed over Rob as he remembered his first view of Mars. God, only eight years ago.

He sighed as he walked away from the window towards the light switch.

'Close the blackout curtains, Charlie, and I'll show you.'

The room was flooded with a kaleidoscope of colour: books and star-charts and pictures of planes filled every inch of wall space. The patchwork quilt on Rob's bed was a riot of blues and greens and reds, painstakingly stitched by his mother. On a small rosewood table by the bed was a hand-sized blue mottled stone, criss-crossed with irregular white lines which looked as if they'd been painted by Klee. Charlie had found it, polished it until it almost glowed in the dark and given it to Rob. Rob picked it up.

'What would happen if I dropped this stone, Charlie?'

'It would hit the table, smash on the floor, make a bloomin' great noise, and Auntie Mary would run up the stairs and blame me.'

'Oh, Charlie,' said Rob, laughing, 'I will miss you.'

'What you mean?'

Rob put the stone down quickly and walked over to his star charts.

'The authorities think it would be … better … safer … if the children from London are … moved … to another place.'

All the colour drained from Charlie's face.

'They're expecting an invasion, you see … it won't be safe here any more.'

Charlie stood very still, staring at the planes on the wall.

'I don't suppose it'll be for very long …' Rob's voice trailed away as he saw the boy sway slightly. 'Charlie?'

There was a long silence, then Charlie walked slowly out of the room and closed the door.

Hours later, Rob was sitting in the lounge with his parents drinking whisky.

'But there's nothing we can do, Rob. He has to go within a fortnight.' Mary was worried by the haunted look on her son's face.

'I've written to his mother and asked her to come to see him before he goes,' John said. 'I've told her I'll give her the money for the journey.'

'Well, that will make him feel better, won't it?'

Mary and John looked at him, startled. It was almost as if he blamed them for sending Charlie away.

'Another drink anyone?' Rob poured himself another large glass before waving the whisky bottle in their faces.

'Rob, don't you think –' Mary stopped abruptly as John shook his head at her.

'Let's hear that chap on the wireless, shall we? – what's he called again, Mary?'

'Priestley, dear.'

'Ah, yes.' John switched on, hoping to hear something that would lighten the mood. JB Priestley's Yorkshire vowels floated round their sitting room, painting a vivid picture of England.

"I've looked out of my house in the country on these marvellous days of sun and blue air and I could see the blaze and bloom of the Californian poppies and the roses in the garden; the twinkling beeches and stately nodding elms – and then, beyond, the lush fields and the round green hills dissolving into the hazy blue of the sky."

Mary and John enjoyed listening to Priestley's reflections on life in his weekly broadcasts. They smiled at each other.

"I've stared at this and I've remembered the terrible news of battle and destruction and I've felt that one or the other couldn't be true.

Sometimes I've felt that I was staring at a beautifully painted silk curtain; and that at any moment it might be torn apart – its flowers, trees and green hills vanishing like smoke to reveal the old Flanders Front, trenches and bomb craters, ruined towns, and the faces of murdered children."

They sat in silence before Mary got up and switched the wireless off.

Rob suddenly leapt from his chair and paced up and down. 'Heard this one?' he shouted at his parents.

What a naughty boy is Heines,
Quite unlike the other tinies,
Always with a loaded whip
Lying snug against his hip

'Robert.' Mary was frightened by the twisted expression on her son's face as he paced the room.

Always having lots of fun
With his automatic gun
Always at the Nazi rallies
Crying 'Murder uber alles.'

'Robert!' John's voice was glacial.

Rob slumped into the chair, cradling his head in his hands. 'I'm sorry …I'm sorry … but you ought to have seen his face when I told him.'

'I know, Rob,' John said, gently. 'We're all fond of Charlie … but there's a war on.'

Rob looked at his parents with the same twisted expression. 'Well, I'd better get back and fight in it then, hadn't I?'

Rob staggered up the stairs at midnight. His head already throbbing from an overload of whisky. Poor little blighter, he thought. Another move. He stood outside Charlie's room for a few seconds, then opened the door quietly to see if he was still awake. The bed was empty.

'Charlie? Where are you?' Rob switched on the light. Charlie's stone collection under the window was gone and so was Charlie.

'Mum? Dad?' Rob raced down the stairs. Headache forgotten. 'Charlie's gone.'

He must have gone to see her, Rob thought as he raced down the road to the Brazier's.

Shit! He fell headlong over a sandbag someone had left on the pavement. He picked himself up and walked carefully, following the white lines painted on the kerbs. The torch battery was running low, hardly any light showed beneath the tissue paper covering the Perspex lens. The shops had run out of batteries. Not a light to be seen in the town. He shivered as he looked up. The 'silence in the starry skies' couldn't comfort him tonight. It was too vast. The sudden cry of an owl punctured the night air and he was locked in loneliness.

Kate heard stones being thrown against her window and looked down in astonishment at Rob's white face. She opened the window.

'Is Charlie with you?' he shouted up at her.

'Shhh – you'll wake everyone – of course not – it's after midnight. What's the matter?'

'He ran off, Kate – after I told him.'

Suddenly Rose's frightened face appeared at the side of Kate's.

'I knew he would. You won't find him.'

Kate looked at her sister in surprise. 'I'll come down. Wait there.'

By the time Kate had opened the door the whole household was awake, Bill grumbling at the disturbance. Hilda got up, telling him to go back to sleep.

'Where's he gone, Rose?' Rob asked her, his whisky breath wafting around the small scullery. Kate frowned as the fumes hit her.

'Dunno.' Rose looked at the floor, the ceiling, the table; anywhere except the circle of faces peering at her.

'Rose, if you don't tell us this instant, I'll get your father up and then there'll be trouble.' Hilda was too exhausted to argue. She had enough to worry about. She hadn't heard from Colin in weeks. She looked at Rob's bleary eyes. At least Mary didn't have to worry about her son being killed at the moment.

Rose saw the no-nonsense expression on her mother's face and gave in. 'I think he'll go to the caves. We hide in them sometimes when we're escaping from the Germans.'

Hilda looked at her daughter. The strange things that went on in that child's head.

'St Clements' Caves?' said Rob, holding his head. It was beginning to throb badly.

Kate went to the pantry and fetched him some aspirins.

'St Clements' Caves in the dark by himself. Oh dear, oh dear,' said Hilda. 'He must be upset.'

Rob got up. 'I'll get Dad's car and drive there.'

Kate and Hilda looked at him in horror.

'In your state – you'll crash.'

Kate stood up quickly. 'I can drive.'

Hilda looked at her daughter in astonishment. 'Since when?'

'Since I joined the WAAFs, Mum.'

'You never told me.'

'You wouldn't have been interested, would you? … come on, he must be frightened.'

'Can I go, Mum? Ple-ese,' Rose pleaded with her mother. Hilda started to say no, but Rose spoke before the word left her lips. 'Only I know where he is.'

It was after one o'clock in the morning by the time they reached the caves. Kate had found the Austin 8 too light to handle after the 30 cwt Bedford truck she had driven on camp – twice. They had nearly come off the road four times as she'd yanked the steering wheel over too hard.

'God – give me a plane, anytime,' Rob said as he climbed out of the car, feeling sick from a combination of whisky and Kate's erratic driving.

They all leaned hard against the wind as it swept in from the sea over the West Hill. They walked towards the caves, hand-in-hand, Rob remembering the tales his father had told him about whisky smugglers hiding their booty there before the customs officers could find them.

'Charlie!' Rob called out as they entered the cave entrance which smelt of age and secrets. 'Charlie!' His voice reverberated off the stone walls.

'I thought it'd be colder at night,' said Rose, thinking how different their secret hide-out looked.

'The thickness of the rock acts as an insulator,' Rob said, automatically.

'I can't believe a child would stay here in the dark by himself.' Kate shivered as she looked at their distorted, elongated shadows on the floor of the cave.

Rob swung the torch around the first tunnel and back to the floor again. 'Which way, Rose?'

Rose had explored all the tunnels with Charlie: they were on two levels; a small upper cavern and an extensive lower one, full of interlocking tunnels. She knew that Charlie would be in the last tunnel in the lower cavern.

Ten minutes later, they found him, lying curled up in a foetal position inside the circle of his precious stones. He was walking along a river bed before the dawn; deep inside his head a path was winding. It was bordered with dense, tortured thorns which punctured his skin. Suddenly, he came to a clearing at the top of the hill. In the distance of the dying moonlight he saw white islands of clouds – in one cloud, a face was forming. A nose. A jaw. Two eyes. Staring. Then he started to scream as the light hit him.

Rob swung the torch onto the floor quickly as Charlie's hazel eyes blinked rapidly in alarm.

'It's okay, Charlie. It's me.'

'And me and Kate,' said Rose quietly. 'I had to bring them, Charlie.'

Charlie backed against the wall. 'I ain't goin' away! I ain't! You can't make me!' His voice trembled. 'I hate you, Rose Brazier – bringing them here!'

'I had to Charlie. Don't be angry with me.' Large tears dripped down Rose's face. 'My Mum made me.'

'I wouldn't have told no one if you was hiding,' Charlie screamed at her. 'I never wanna see you no more! You cow!'

Rose crumpled onto the floor of the cave, howling. 'I couldn't help it, Charlie. I couldn't! I couldn't! I couldn't!'

Rob and Kate looked at each other in desperation.

'Take Rose back to the car, will you, Kate?' Rob shouted over Rose's wailing.

'How can we get back without a torch?'

'Have this.' He gave her the torch.

'You can't stay here in the dark.'

'We won't be in the dark.' Rob brought out a candle and his cigarette lighter from his pocket. He lit the candle. 'Now go on.'

Kate pulled Rose up off the floor, still crying, and dragged her out of Charlie's tunnel.

Charlie's curled body flickered in the candlelight, his back against the sandstone, his head averted. In one hand, he held the mottled blue stone he had polished and given to Rob. Rob lit a cigarette and saw the tremor in his fingers shadowed on the wall of the cave. There was a long silence as the smoke swirled around them.

Finally, Rob began to speak. 'This is a true story, Charlie … There was once a boy called Joshua who lived in America – the southern states of America. He lived with his mother in a hut on a big plantation – they were cotton pickers. The work was hard. Picking cotton made his hands bleed, but he didn't complain because his mother didn't complain. He was twelve. His mother came into their hut one day and told him he had to leave the plantation because a man had bought him.'

Charlie's head jerked on the word 'bought', but he didn't speak.

'Joshua was frightened. He didn't want to leave his mother or the plantation. This was his home, but his mother told him that if he didn't go, the Master would beat her. Now Joshua loved his mother and didn't want her beaten, but he couldn't understand why he had to leave. So she told him about slavery – about how slaves were bought and sold like cattle.'

'That ain't right!' Charlie argued, looking at Rob for the first time.

'And Joshua's eyes filled with tears as he looked at his mother, but she told him he must be brave. He mustn't let the white folks see him cry. Joshua kept sobbing into his mother's dress, frightened that he would never see her again. And his mother held him tight and told him to be strong and wait – wait until she came to find him.'

'And did she?' Charlie asked, quickly.

'Oh yes,' Rob answered quietly, watching smoke drift around the cavern.

Charlie thought about the story for some time before he spoke.

'Why was Joshua a slave?'

'Because his great-great-grandfather was taken from Africa as a boy and sent to America, I suppose.'

'I don't mean that … I mean why did people let it start?'

Rob leaned against the wall of the cave to give him time. 'I think because people are greedy. The slave trade was a way of making a lot of unscrupulous people a lot of money quickly.'

There was silence for a long time as Charlie stroked the silk surface of the blue stone.

'I don't like a lot of people.'

'No, nor do I. But there are people I like … you're one of them.'

'So why you sending me away?'

'I'm not – the government is. They're trying to protect children.'

'So why isn't Rose being sent away?'

Rob couldn't think of an answer.

'It doesn't make sense,' Charlie said, studying Rob's face.

Rob was back in his Maths class, trying to think of a logical answer. It suddenly came to him.

'No, it doesn't … What if I ask Uncle John to contact the authorities to say that you'll go if all the local children from the Hastings area are sent away too.'

Charlie looked at him for a long time. 'If I say yes, you'll come and see me, won't you? Wherever I am. Solemn promise?'

'Solemn promise, Charlie. If – later – you're sent away by the authorities, I'll visit you every leave I have – wherever you are … How's that?'

Charlie's face looked drained in the flickering candlelight, but he nodded.

Rob stood up. He didn't know how long he'd been sitting cross-legged on the sandy floor of the cave, but his legs felt full of lead.

'Let's go home, Charlie.'

'Where's that?' Charlie's hazel eyes were immense as he stared up at Rob. 'You will come and find me, won't you? Wherever I am?'

'Wherever you are, I'll find you,' Rob answered.

And the blue stone shimmered in the candlelight as Charlie gave it back to Rob.

When they returned home, John and Mary listened to Rob, silently disagreeing with his idea, but John told Charlie he would write to a friend of his in the Education Department. Then Charlie, Mary and John all went to bed, totally exhausted. Rob stayed downstairs, pacing up and down, unable to sleep. He knew how important it was to Charlie that he keep his word.

Charlie went into a dead sleep within seconds of hitting the pillow. Rob checked on him before he went to bed himself. Charlie lay on his back with one arm thrown across his face as if he was trying to protect himself, even while he slept. Rob felt a profound sense of helplessness as he looked down at the vulnerable boy. He wanted to hug him, to tell him there wasn't anything to worry about. But there was.

He walked over to Charlie's bedroom window and looked out at the night. A sudden gust of wind swept through the garden, making the pots and pans clatter in the dustbins and the windows rattle. The house didn't like wind. Rob remembered all the sleepless nights he'd spent as a child, listening to little creaking, straining sounds. He had spent most of his childhood thinking the house was trying to move slowly down the road.

He looked back at Charlie. He hadn't stirred.

All this anguish, he thought – and I'm not even related to him.

Rob got up at dawn. He'd spent a restless night, tossing and turning. He passed his unshaven reflection in the mirror with a cursory glance. He couldn't look like that.

He crept downstairs, vowing that whisky would never pass his lips again, put the kettle on and walked out into the garden. A curlew winged past his head, its echoing voice growing fainter as it flew towards the sea.

The dawn had shrouded the garden in mist: cold, clammy and very still. Tiny droplets covered every plant, flower and tree. Rob shivered and went back into the house for some aspirins, thinking that this was no rosy-fingered dawn. He sat in the kitchen and watched a gentle breeze send swirls of vapour curling and moving in the air, slowly warmed by the sun. The light gradually grew brighter as Rob hugged his mug of tea and thought about Charlie. So much hidden in such a small body. He had never spoken about his family. Not once. Rob didn't hear the clock recording the seconds on the Victorian mantelpiece. He was lost in fantasies from Charlie's past.

By the time he'd returned to the present, the mist had gone and the sun was warming the earth. He walked back into the garden. Threads so fine as to be almost invisible spanned the branches of the beech trees, suspending spider webs as large as dinner plates, which the mist had touched with scintillating beauty. He saw water diamonds holding the sunlight in countless tiny globes hanging from every silken thread, and within their glistening form each drop mirrored the world around it. How could such perfection exist in such an imperfect world?

A hand on his shoulder. His father stood in carpet slippers and striped pyjamas behind him. His grey eyes blood-shot from lack of sleep.

'I'm sorry about last night, Dad.'

'Charlie's a difficult child.'

'He's frightened.'

John looked at his son before speaking, reading the gauntness in his unshaven cheeks. 'You know he has to go, Rob. Whether it's next week or next month. You're just postponing the time.'

There was a long pause.

'He's not our son. He'll have to go back to his own family some time.'

'But why doesn't he talk about his family, Dad? It's not natural, is it?'

'I don't know. His house was squalid, but …'

Rob waited.

'Hundreds of children live in such conditions and still love their homes and parents. I just don't know, Rob.'

'There may be a reason why he shouldn't be sent back.' Rob stared at his father. 'Surely we should find out?'

John walked slowly back into the kitchen for some breakfast.

'I've got surgery in half an hour. I've hundreds of patients who need my time … what can I do? Tell me?'

'I'll make you some toast … I don't know, Dad. But you always sorted things out when I was a boy.'

'Robert – there wasn't a war on then and you're my son.'

Rob became very quiet as he made his father's breakfast. John squeezed his eyes hard; they were hurting as usual.

'Look – I'll ring up Norman King, the Chief Education Officer, and tell him we'll look after Charlie until the other children are sent away … All right? … That's all I can do, Rob. Don't forget his mother is coming to see him next week. Have a talk with her.'

Rob sat down with his father. They ate their breakfast in silence.

Chapter 19

`My body is a floating weed,
severed at the roots.'

Ono no Komachi. (834-880)
Japanese Poet

They met Charlie's mother from Warrior Square Station. Rob was shocked at her appearance. A small, emaciated woman stood on the platform, wearing a shabby black dress which moved, seemingly, without her. Rob and Charlie walked over to her, not knowing they both wore the same nervous smiles.

'Hello, Mrs Slater. I'm Robert Adams. My father came to see you in London.' Rob shook her hand and was disturbed by the feel of the dry, hard bone he held.

Charlie's mother looked about fifty, although Charlie had told him she was only twenty-nine. Her face had the caved-in look of consumptives he had seen in his father's medical books. Vague hazel eyes, exactly the same colour as her son's, but with none of his animation, stared in surprise at Charlie.

'Charlie? It never is! – he ain't that big or handsome.'

Charlie looked deeply embarrassed as she threw stick arms around him.

'Hallo Mum. How's me brothers?'

His mother's eyes became guarded as she looked from Charlie to Rob. 'They all right, luv… Mickie and Alf's with a nice family in Coventry, an' Jimmy's with a nice family in Hornchurch, I think.'

'You don't know?' Rob looked down at her in surprise.

'Can't read the letters, luv... an' ... I ain't been too good lately.'

As if to prove the point she started coughing profusely, bringing out a dirty grey handkerchief from a voluminous pocket and hawking into it loudly. Everyone on the platform stared.

Charlie looked quickly at Rob, his face scarlet.

They were all in the lounge, drinking tea, everyone sitting on the edge of their seats. Charlie looked as if he was having a tooth extracted each time he glanced at his mother. The awful thing was, Rob thought, they could smell her from across the room – like rancid meat. Her skin was coated with layers of grime; her hair, a grey mat of grease snaking down her back.

Mary tried valiantly to keep the conversation alive while Charlie's mother stared around the room in awe, a china cup of tea balanced precariously on a bony knee. Charlie's eyes followed each trembling movement.

'I ain't gonna fuckin' believe this tomorrow, Charlie. You livin' in a house like this. Blimey, you fallen on yer feet, ain't you, luv?'

Charlie looked quickly at Mary.

'Was the journey down very bad, Mrs Slater?' Mary was fighting the urge to clamp a handkerchief across her nose and mouth.

'Don't know – ain't never been on a train. They always slow?' She suddenly saw the garden and got up excitedly, the china cup clattering onto the carpet. Charlie gazed in horror at the brown stains spreading across the Axminster. He suddenly leapt up to get a cloth from the kitchen.

'Oh – sorry, luv,' Mrs Slater said, as she walked over to the window to look at the garden. 'Fancy – a park outside yer back door. Ain't you lucky... I loves trees.'

Mary rushed to open the French windows wide and stood outside in the clean, June air, breathing deeply. 'Yes, so do I. Perhaps Charlie can show you around.'

They turned back to look for him. He was desperately scrubbing at the stains on the carpet. 'Charlie – it's all right. Come and show your mother around the garden. I'll do that.'

'It's nearly finished now, Auntie Mary.' He carried on scrubbing, while Mary stood awkwardly at the side of his mother.

Rob walked over to him and whispered, 'For God's sake – leave it, Charlie.' He took the scrubbing brush off him. 'Go and talk to your mother – you haven't seen her for nearly a year.'

Charlie's eyes darted towards his mother. Rob noticed he was breathing too quickly.

'I'll sit here, Charlie, and read the newspaper while you show her around, all right? … We can go and see the Heinkel if you want … after your mother's gone.'

Charlie gave Rob a small smile and walked out into the garden: his back, a ramrod.

'Come and look at the veg I planted, Mum.' Charlie walked down the end of the garden where all his vegetables were planted in neat rows. His mother followed behind him; her cough a saw, slicing the air.

'You did all this, luv?' she said when the coughing stopped. 'Talk about digging for fuckin' victory – it's Australia you'll be.'

'Don't swear, Mum.'

His mother looked at him in astonishment. 'What? – I ain't swored. What you mean?'

Charlie looked at the lines of peas he'd planted.

'Y's all right, ain't you, luv? I don't wan' you to think I don't … think about you – 'cos I does. But London's no place for kids, is it? Got everything here, ain't you?'

'Yeah – everything.'

'That's good, init? … have to sit down, luv. Feel a bit off colour these days.'

'I'll get you a garden chair. Wait there.' Charlie raced into the garden shed and brought back a chair before his mother could walk back to the house.

'Blimey – that were quick, luv.' She sat down heavily as another bout of coughing racked her. 'Fuckin' cough. Drives me barmy.' She squinted up at him standing underneath the enormous russet beech tree. 'Gawd – you don't look like me Charlie no more with all that meat on you… Yer Dad wouldn't know you.'

Charlie's face jerked.

'He joined the Army last winter. Best thing, init?'

Charlie picked the bark off the beech tree.

'Remember Mrs Strong, luv – the one in the end terrace? – 'er husband copped it in Dunkirk and old Mrs Fosse – the one with the gammy leg? – her son's missing somewhere. Street ain't the same no more, luv. Bleedin' quiet it is. No kids playin' nowhere.'

'What time is your train back, Mrs Slater?' Mary called out from the house. 'Would you like to stay for tea?'

Charlie looked quickly at his mother. Just as she started to speak another spasm of coughing shook her narrow frame. They all watched her hawk into the dirty handkerchief again. Charlie shuddered.

'Don't think so, Mrs Adams. Not too good to be honest.'

Charlie ran up to Mary. 'Could I make Mum some sandwiches for the journey, Auntie Mary?'

'Of course you can, Charlie. I'll help you.'

Rob looked at his mother in amazement. She never left guests to fend for themselves. Mary raised her eyebrows at him and then looked at Charlie's mother sitting alone in the garden. He could feel pinpricks of resentment over his body as he walked towards Mrs Slater.

'You must miss Charlie, Mrs Slater … well … all your sons.'

She looked up at Rob quickly. 'Yeah – I does.' Then her eyes darted away. 'The house is ever so quiet without the kids.'

An awkward silence.

'Is Charlie close to his father?' Rob asked, watching her reaction.

'What you mean – close?'

'Well – did he take him out? … Did they do things together?'

'Like what?' She sat very still.

Did she really not know what he was talking about, Rob thought.

'Well, things like cricket, football, swimming … you know … that sort of thing.' The conversation was deflating like a balloon.

'Naw – not our Frank – didn't have the time, did he?'

'Was he working long hours then?'

'What Frank! Naw – 'e were always out of work, luv.' She wasn't really listening to Rob now, but looking round the garden. 'Oh, look at 'em flowers on top of the shelter. Ain't they pretty? What are they?'

'So if he wasn't working, why didn't he take Charlie and his brothers out sometimes?'

She looked at him as if she was talking to a retarded child. 'Didn't have no money, luv – he were eiver lookin' for work or up the dog track. … Ooh – tell a lie – our Charlie did go out with 'im once – to the dog track when he were eight. Best forgotten that, luv – lost all our money.' She suddenly shivered. 'Still, war's changed all that, ain't it? Got money comin' in regular from the army now and I don't have the boys to think about.'

She saw Rob's expression change and added quickly. 'Course I think of 'em all the time, but London's no place for kids in war, is it? Look at our Charlie. He don't want for nothing here, do he?'

'No – he's got everything,' Rob said, as he stormed off back into the house.

They waved until the train was out of sight, steam covering them in a layer of grey smoke.

'Charlie – can I ask about your parents?'

Charlie stared at the smoke as they walked out of the station and shook his head.

'Okay – remember my promise?'

A frown creased Charlie's face.

'The Heinkel at Summerfields.'

'Oh, yeah!'

He bounded out of the station and Rob suddenly realised Charlie was wandering between two worlds – and didn't fit into either.

They walked up the road towards Summerfields: a beautiful white Regency house which was being used as the Town Hall. The grounds were milling with people who had all paid 6d to see a German plane.

In the distance was a Heinkel He 111, just like the one Rob had shot down. Charlie ran over to it.

'Oi!' shouted the man collecting admission fees. 'You got to get a ticket!'

'It's all right – he's with me,' Rob said, giving the man a shilling.

Rob walked over the grass towards Charlie who stood in the front of the German bomber with his mouth open.

'Blimey, Rob – you knocked this big whopper out of the sky?'

Rob could hardly believe it himself when he looked up at the large plane.

'How many crew can it carry? How fast can it go? How many machine guns has it got?'

Rob laughed at Charlie's rapid-fire questions. 'You know what you remind me of, Charlie? The Elephant's Child in the *Just So* stories with his "satiable curiosity."'

'Don't laugh at me!' Charlie looked hurt.

'I'm not.' Rob smiled down at him and tousled his hair. 'Look – that's where they carry their 440 lbs of bombs.'

A small band of boys had gathered around the plane and were listening to Rob. One of the bigger boys looked at Rob suspiciously.

'How come you know about Nazi planes, Mister?'

''Cos he's a Spitfire pilot. He shot down one of those.' Charlie looked at the boys proudly.

'Go on – he never!' one of the smaller boys protested.

Charlie's face went red with anger.

'Tell 'em, Rob.'

'Charlie!'

The last thing Rob wanted was a crowd of little boys following him around all afternoon, then he saw the frustration on Charlie's face.

'All right. I shot down a Heinkel over the English Channel four weeks ago, lads, and had to parachute out of my Spitfire. There were flames coming out of it that high.' Rob put his arms high in the air. The boys' mouths dropped open.

'Inside that cockpit were five Germans blasting away with their 7.9 mm machine guns right at me. Duga-duga-duga-duga-duga.'

Rob's machine-gun noises were attracting a small crowd. 'At the back of the cockpit,' Rob pointed to a window at the rear of the plane, 'is a small seat … that's where they sometimes carry an extra gunner. If they'd been carrying one that day, I wouldn't be standing here talking to you.' He paused for effect. 'I'd be dead.'

The boys looked up at Rob in awe.

'Tell us how you shot him down, Mister,' one of the small boys shouted.

Charlie looked as if he was going to burst with pride.

Suddenly, the distorted screech of a Tannoy pierced the air. The Chief of the Hastings Fire Brigade, Mr Abrahams, was standing on a platform waiting to give an explanatory talk on aircraft.

'Ladies and gentlemen – thank you all for coming here today in aid of our Spitfire Fund. As you can see we have a Heinkel on display which was shot down only two weeks ago.'

'Could be yours, Rob!' Charlie's eyes glowed.

'As you can see, ladies and gentlemen – this Heinkel has seen a lot of action.'

They could all see that the side of the plane was riddled with bullet holes.

'Our boys have been shooting down planes like this for over a year now. Unfortunately, the Hun has been shooting down a few of our planes too. That's why we need your contribution to the Spitfire Fund.'

'What's he know about planes?' Charlie said to Rob. 'Bet he's never been in one in his life.'

'This bomber carried a bomb load of 550 lbs and was armed with up to eight machine-guns,' the Chief of the Fire Brigade continued.

The boys all looked at Rob as he shook his head.

'He's got it wrong, hasn't he, Rob?' Charlie looked annoyed. He suddenly ran over to the platform and shouted up at Mr Abrahams. 'There's a real pilot here what could tell you a thing or two.'

The man looked down at Charlie and gave a nervous laugh. Rob walked over to Charlie to drag him away.

'He's a real Spitfire pilot, he is!' shouted Charlie pointing at Rob. He turned to the crowd. 'Shot down he was and nearly killed.'

'Charlie!'

A ripple of interest ran around the crowd. Mr Abrahams looked down at Rob.

'Is the lad telling the truth, young man?'

'Well – yes – I'm a Spitfire pilot.' Rob was acutely embarrassed under the scrutiny of the crowd.

'Ladies and gentlemen,' the man boomed over the Tannoy, 'we are privileged to have a Spitfire pilot among us today. A big round of applause for one of our boys.' He started clapping and everyone, looking at Rob, joined in.

'I'll kill you when we get home, Charlie,' Rob muttered under his breath.

'Could I ask you to say a few words about your experiences of flying for the Spitfire Fund, young man?' Mr Abrahams continued.

Rob shook his head, but Charlie pushed him onto the platform.

'I'm …er… not very good at making speeches,' Rob said into the Tannoy.

'The RAF's not very good at flying close to beaches, neither,' shouted a soldier from the crowd. 'Where was you when our lads needed help?'

A wave of tension oscillated up and down the crowd.

'Flying over Dunkirk trying to shoot down the Luftwaffe,' Rob shouted back.

'Oh yes! Well why didn't our lot see you then? We saw a lot of bloody Germans, I can tell you. Perhaps the RAF liked it out to sea better!' The soldier looked around at the crowd. 'Hundreds I saw left on the beaches. Don't talk to me about the bloody RAF.'

Rob was trembling as he walked off the platform.

'He was shot down he was – nearly killed.' Charlie, an arrow of frustrated rage, yelled at the crowd. 'And …and … he shot down a Heinkel … Rob – tell 'em!'

But Rob was walking away from Summerfields, down the road towards the sea.

'Why didn't you tell them, Rob? Why'd you let them think you were a coward?'

Rob was speeding along the promenade with Charlie running at the side of him.

'Because I couldn't describe what it was like firing at Germans through smoke and oil and flames, Charlie, that's why.'

'Why not?'

Rob didn't answer.

'At school, it's only me and Rose has a Spitfire pilot in the family.' Charlie looked quickly at Rob. 'You know what I mean.'

'Yes.'

Rob gradually slowed down to look at the red-orbed sun blazing across the sea. Some black-headed gulls gathered together in the sky, wheeling and calling before flying over the tall Victorian terraced houses on the sea front.

They stopped in front of a marble war memorial and looked up at the black inscription: *Erected by the inhabitants of this borough to the memory of their brave fellow townsmen who fell in the South African War 1899 to 1902*.

Charlie looked up at the wording on the top of it. *Borough of* --- 'Looks funny without the name, don't it?'

During the last month they had seen the removal of all road and rail signs which had been creating chaos on the roads and train stations. Shop signs had been painted over to remove any trace of the name Hastings or St Leonards. Even the trolley bus coming towards them enigmatically stated --- *and District Ltd.*

'And it's a waste of time.' Rob pointed across the road. 'We can still buy postcards over there, Charlie, saying "Welcome to Hastings".' He shook his head at the lack of logic in so many of the preparations for the invasion.

'Why does the government allow that then?'

'God knows. The only thing it might do – knowing how logical the Germans are – is confuse them even more.'

'How?'

Rob smiled down at Charlie.

'A German would believe that anything so illogical and stupid must be a trap.'

'You know a lot about Germans, don't you?'

'Only some,' Rob said, thinking of the hours he'd spent with Axel's family, wandering around the Lüneberger Heide in the summer, returning in the evening, hot and thirsty, to drink the wonderful home-made lemonade Axel's mother always made for them in her large kitchen.

'Rob – you know in Summerfields—?' Charlie suddenly stopped as Rob shook his head. They walked along in silence.

Through the barbed wire, Charlie could see white caps on the waves.

'Wish we could walk on the beach … Me and Rosie saw a storm last winter from my bedroom window. Never seen nothing like it before – all the waves crashing over the sea wall. Went down to the beach after – there was this long line of flotsam and jetsam.' Charlie looked at Rob. 'Learnt that from Miss Brown. You ought to have seen the things we collected for our nature table. It was heaving.'

Rob smiled. He could imagine Charlie carting the whole beach into the classroom if he could.

'What's Miss Brown like?'

Charlie thought about this as he walked along. 'Nice … she doesn't make fun of any one. And she never gets cross – even when we all answer at the same time – tell a lie – did see her really angry once – when Tony Browne hit Carole in the playground. Blimey – she was like a tiger then – she sprang at him.'

'Tigress … I don't know how she can cope with all of you. One's enough.'

'Yeah, know what you mean. They're not all like me, Rob. Some of them are real pains.'

Rob laughed just as the narrow pencil-shape of a Dornier came out of a cloud at high speed and flew low along the coastline. Rob and Charlie were blinded for a second by a wink of lights. Before either of them had time to react, the plane disappeared into a large cloud. They stood on the promenade, stunned.

'Blimey! – what's that?'

'That,' said Rob heavily, 'was a Dornier taking aerial reconnaissance photographs of our coast-line for Adolf.'

For once, Charlie was speechless.

When they got home Rob rang up the Military Headquarters in Hastings and reported what he had seen. He could hear Charlie in the kitchen shouting excitedly to his mother.

'It was that close, Auntie Mary. I could see the colour of the pilot's eyes – green they was.'

'"Were,"' said Mary. 'You couldn't have, Charlie.'

'Honest – I did – they was – were – green.'

Rob, standing in the hall listening, felt his heart thump hard in his chest. It couldn't be. It was impossible. He was in the Hastings bathing pool with Axel in 1936. German swimmers were competing against British swimmers in 'Europe's finest bathing pool.' The Germans, all young, tall Aryan types were wearing red, blue and black bathing trunks: Nazi colours. Axel was digging him in the ribs, cheering, as the Germans won and

Rob pushed him off the bench. Axel had laughed up at him with his startling sea-green eyes, exactly the same colour as the pool.

'Did you get through?' Mary asked Rob as he walked into the kitchen.

'Yes, they're going to pass the information on to Fighter Command.' He threw himself down in a chair. 'It makes me wonder – how many other reconnaissance planes they've been sending over the South coast.'

'It doesn't look good, does it?' his mother said.

'No.'

There was a long silence.

Mary thought of the posters that had been put up all over the town:

IF THE INVADER COMES: WHAT TO DO AND HOW TO DO IT. IF THE GERMANS COME, BY PARACHUTE, AEROPLANE OR SHIP, YOU MUST REMAIN WHERE YOU ARE. THE ORDER IS 'STAY PUT'.

THINK BEFORE YOU ACT. BUT THINK ALWAYS OF YOUR COUNTRY BEFORE YOU THINK OF YOURSELF.

'Mum … I've been recalled to my squadron.' Rob's words chilled the room. 'I have to report for a Medical on Wednesday.'

Mary hurried to open her recipe book and started to weigh the ingredients out carefully. Charlie's face went white. He stared at Rob in panic.

'But that's the day after tomorrow! You can't go yet! Didn't y' hear, Auntie Mary? What you doing?' He watched her in bewilderment, putting sugar and margarine and flour into a large white bowl.

'He has to go, Charlie. He's in the RAF … Now go and get me some potatoes and carrots for dinner, please.'

Charlie slouched into the garden. He didn't see Rob gather his mother into his arms.

After dinner, they all sat in the lounge drinking coffee and brandy. Charlie had been allowed to stay up as long as he didn't talk through Churchill's speech. They heard the Prime Minister's sonorous tones flood the lounge, telling them of Hitler's plans for invading the British Isles. To quell any feelings of panic, the Prime Minister assured the nation that everyone would do their duty and they would *'ride out the storm and outlive the menace of tyranny, if necessary alone.'*

'Alone! – surely America will come to our aid, John?' Mary asked him.

John motioned her to silence as Churchill stated emphatically that Britain would fight the enemy on seas and oceans, beaches and landing grounds, fields and streets and hills. *'We shall never surrender,'* he concluded, and the conviction in his voice made them convinced of the truth of his words.

John got up and switched the wireless off, but Churchill's speech echoed round the room. They sat still for some time, trying to digest it before Charlie broke the silence.

'Blimey, we're going to fight in a lot of places.'

They all smiled at Charlie's incredulous expression.

'Mr Churchill sometimes gets carried away by his own rhetoric,' John said. He saw Charlie's puzzled expression and added: 'Big words, but I think we need them and strong actions if we're to win this fight.'

'As long as the actions are focused on the enemy, Dad, not us. I don't like Bevin's New Emergency Act – it practically gives the government authority over everything and everyone.' Rob frowned as he looked at his father.

'I don't see what else they can do, – not with the threat of invasion looming.'

Rob looked dubious. 'Smacks of Fascism to me – unlimited power over people and property.'

'It does to me too,' Mary said. 'I certainly don't like the idea of Ernest Bevin having unlimited power over me.'

John smiled at her. 'That, my dear, would be utterly impossible.'

She smiled back at him.

Charlie kept looking from face to face as they spoke.

'What's Fascism?'

Mary and John turned to Rob.

'Oh, thanks.' He scratched his head trying to think how to explain the concept to Charlie.

'Remember you telling me about a boy in your class hitting a girl. Well, Hitler's a bit like that – only a hundred times worse. He doesn't want to hit one person, but whole countries … A Fascist is a person who never listens to ideas of tolerance, Charlie … he just reaches for a black uniform and a weapon.' Rob looked at his father. 'Simplistic I know.'

'Do you remember me telling you about a meeting I went to at the White Rock years ago given by the BUF, Mary?' said John.

Mary nodded. 'Of course I do … in 1935. I was worried about you going.'

'What's the BUF, Uncle John?'

'The British Union of Fascists.'

'You went to a Fascist meeting?' Charlie's eyes bulged in astonishment. 'But Hitler's a Fascist!'

'It's good to know how the enemy thinks, Charlie,' Rob said.

John looked up at the ceiling, trying to remember. '"*What design would I be …*" Oh dear, oh dear, old age is creeping up too fast.'

'"*What design would I be forming if I were the enemy?*"' Rob smiled at his father who'd given him Frederick the Great's *Principles of War* just before he had joined the RAF.

'I'll never forget the speaker's voice at that meeting. Very nasal and upper class. A man called William Joyce. Hundreds of blackshirts got out of coaches and walked into the White Rock Pavilion and lined the walls and gangways of the hall. A man in front of me with a German accent stood up and asked Joyce to outline Fascist policy. Joyce wouldn't answer, so the German kept repeating his question over and over until four blackshirts dragged him out of the hall. I heard him shouting all the way out. *"Nicht alle Deutschen sind Faschisten! Ich bin Deutscher Jude."'* John forestalled Charlie's question. '"Not all Germans are Fascists. I am a German Jew." I don't know what happened to the man … I can only guess.'

John turned to Charlie. 'That's the face of Fascism, Charlie.'

'Then we got to win, haven't we?'

'Yes – we can't afford any more Dunkirks.' John turned to Rob. 'Was it a glorious retreat as Churchill says or a shambles?'

'A bit of both, Dad.' Rob looked at his mother, knowing that she'd want to hear the truth. 'I flew over the beach one day and saw a hundred Luftwaffe formation firing their canon onto our men.'

They all sat very still, watching Rob's face. 'The men were waiting in the sand dunes – their only protection – for anything that looked remotely like a boat to appear. Most of them were mown down as they ran towards the water. We couldn't do anything. I remember that.'

Rob's knuckles cracked through the silence.

'Doris' sons could have been there,' Mary said. 'I honestly believe she blames me because the RAF didn't save them. I saw her yesterday and she looked the other way.'

'Well, she's not alone in blaming the RAF, Mum,' Rob said, looking at Charlie.

'But that's not fair, is it? You was out every day trying to protect them.'

'Yes, but sometimes we were over the beaches too late, Charlie – the Luftwaffe had left a trail of destruction, and sometimes, too early – we left before they arrived. We could only stay on patrol for a limited time, you see. We had to make sure we had enough fuel to fly back to England. Other times it was a nightmare of unidentified planes swirling around each other in a haze of smoke at high speed.'

They didn't notice Mary pick at her nails.

'How can you hit the enemy when you're flying so fast?' Charlie asked him.

'Remember you asking me about gravity?' Charlie nodded, and Rob reached into his jacket pocket and brought out the mottled blue stone with the irregular white lines running around it.

He held it above Charlie's head and suddenly released it.

'Catch!'

Charlie's hand shot out and caught the stone, mid-plummet.

'You saw how the stone dropped, Charlie – gravity pulled it down from my hand into yours. Now if that was a bullet tearing out from my guns at 2,000 mph, it would still drop through gravity, even if only imperceptibly.'

'What?'

'Slightly… But after about 300 yards, as muzzle velocity diminishes,' Rob could see another question forming on Charlie's lips, 'the speed slows down, Charlie – and the bullet begins to arc downwards.' Rob drew an arc in the air with his finger. 'Look I'll show you – Stand over by the tapestry screen and pretend to be a Focke-Wulf.'

Charlie ran over to the screen and stood with his arms out at right angles and bent his body.

'How's that?'

They all laughed as he peered up at them.

'I'd recognise you anywhere, but you're not going to see bent like the Hunchback of Notre Dame … Stand up … Now I'm a Spitfire closing in on my target.' Rob walked towards Charlie. 'Obviously the closer I get to you, the better my aim. However, I can't get too close to you because the slip-stream from your propellers makes it very difficult to hold the Spit steady – and I might even flip over on my back. So I have to judge very carefully how near the enemy I can get without being in his slip-stream … Walk across the carpet slowly, Charlie, and as you walk, get lower and lower … Now I've got to work out where you'll be in a number of seconds from now and fire – not at you – but at the place I think you'll be.' Rob brought up his right hand with two fingers extended and pointed them at a bowl of yellow marigolds just as Charlie crouched in front of them. 'Do you see?'

'Blimey – you got to remember all that before you fire a gun? Don't wanna to be a fighter pilot any more.'

They laughed at Charlie's horrified expression.

'Anyway, young man,' John said, looking at the clock. 'Enough of aerodynamics. It's bed-time.'

'What about a cup of tea first, Uncle John?'

'Charlie – upstairs,' said Mary. Charlie looked into her resolute face and submitted to a greater force.

'All right, Auntie Mary.' He walked over and kissed her on the cheek and then stood still, looking at John.

'Thanks for ringing up that man for me, Uncle John.'

'That's all right, Charlie. Now up to bed.'

Charlie hovered at the door, then suddenly bounded across the room and kissed John's cheek. 'Night, Uncle John.' He turned to Rob. 'See you in a minute.'

Mary and John could still feel the imprint of his kiss on their cheek as Charlie hurtled up the stairs.

The walls of Charlie's bedroom were covered with pictures of planes, stars and a large map of Europe. He was plotting the progress of the war. He looked at the expanse of blue water on his map. That's where Goering's Luftwaffe had been attacking British conveys, Charlie had read in the newspaper. Goering was obviously trying to lure the RAF into the channel so that they could be picked off by his Messerschmitts.

'Don't let them do it, Winny,' he muttered to the map.

Charlie had pictures of all the enemy planes on his walls. He studied the picture of a Focke-Wulf, trying to imagine it as Rob had seen it. Rob had told him it didn't show the Focke as it really was: its pale yellow body, greyish-green back or the big black crosses outlined in white. Pictures, he'd told Charlie, gave no hint of the quivering of the wings fined down for speed or the curious nose-down flying attitude. Charlie knew he would be invaluable as a reconnaissance expert.

If only I wasn't so young, he thought.

His foot touched *King Solomon's Mines* lying open on the floor and he threw himself onto his bed to read it. His bookshelves were heaving with all the books Rob had given him from his boyhood collection. Ten minutes later, Charlie didn't hear Rob coming up the stairs; he was dreaming of finding the map with the whereabouts of the Mines: *"with my own eyes have I seen the countless diamonds stored in Solomon's treasure chamber behind the white Death; but through the treachery of Gagoo the witch-finder I might bring nought away, scarcely my life ..."*

Rob walked in to see Charlie's eyes racing across pages of adventure.

'Enjoying it?'

Charlie closed the book quickly, his eyes enormous in the gathering dusk of the room as he looked up at Rob.

'Yeah ...what's "nought" mean?'

'Nothing.'

A small silence.

'What time you leaving on Wednesday?'

Rob walked over to the window and watched Venus lighting up the sky.

'Early, Charlie.'

'Can I ask you something?'

Rob nodded, his eyes on the stars.

'Is Kate going with you?'

A long silence filled the room. Rob continued to look at the stars, wondering at Charlie's ability to cut through all the layers of protection people built around themselves.

'Yes.'

'Why?'

Rob pulled the curtains across the window. 'Put on the bedside lamp, will you?'

A pale circle of light lit up Charlie's eyes as he stared at Rob.

'We want some time together by ourselves before we go back to duty.'

'Do you love her?'

'That's a very personal question.'

'Yes, but do you?'

Rob looked at Charlie's intent face for some time before answering.

'Yes.'

'What's it feel like?'

'Painful.'

Chapter 20

'Errors, like straws upon the surface flow,
He who would search for
Pearls must dive below.'

John Dryden. (1631- 1700)
Prologue. All for Love

'I can hardly recognise it, Rob.'

Kate had walked through Hyde Park many times with her Aunt Jean, her mother's sister, when she was a little girl while her Uncle Arthur played cricket.

Now the park was dissected by deep trenches, and covered at intervals with high mounds of red-brown earth to prevent any landing of hostile planes.

Another corner of the park had been divided into allotments. 'Not as good as Charlie's output,' Rob said, looking at the vegetables growing in the sunshine.

Kate wrinkled up her nose as she smelt Hyde Park Police Piggery from 200 yards away.

'How can people like pigs?'

'They're intelligent and clean ... so I've heard.' Rob answered, laughing as the wind blew the full pungency of the Piggery in their direction. A young ATS Private walked past them, arm-in-arm with an older woman, who had the same laughing eyes and Kate felt as dirty as dust. She had told her Aunt and Uncle that she was travelling back to camp that day.

But then, she thought, how could I tell them I'm going to spend the night with Rob … losing my virginity.

They walked past the normality of a mown lawn and bright splashes of scarlet and gold dahlias from numerous flowerbeds burst over them. If Kate focused her eyes only on this part of the park, looking towards the heavy foliage of copper beeches and sycamores, she could still believe she was a little girl. Then she noticed people staring at them. A young WAAF and a Flying Officer. Did they know? She bent down to tie the laces of her heavy black shoes to disguise the colour in her face. The sweat was running down the back of her uniform. It was so hot.

'Are you all right?' Rob's voice above her sounded distant.

'Fine … let's go to Speakers' Corner – I used to love it there.'

They walked around an almost derelict bandstand. Grouped in conversational positions were discarded iron chairs, where once music lovers had sat. It had a bald look, Kate thought, and then realised all the railings had been removed for the war effort. Among a heavy cluster of trees, half-hidden, they saw an enormous searchlight.

The park was crowded with people listening to the philosophers of Speakers' Corner. An orator on every rostrum. Rob and Kate were just about to walk on when they were arrested by the oratory of an earnest young man with startlingly bushy eyebrows and limp, long hair which kept falling over his eyes each time he gesticulated. As his hands moved in never-ending circles, his eyes constantly disappeared. A sign in front of him said Michael Foot.

'Intern the lot – I keep reading in the newspapers. Why?'

''Cos they're foreigners, you stupid bugger,' someone piped up, laughing.

'But aren't we wasting vital work-force?' he asked the crowd.

The crowd waited for his answer.

'Goebbels runs the most efficient propaganda campaign the world has ever seen.'

'How d'you know? You a Fascist?'

'Just listen. Goebbels has the sense to realise that if he wants a propaganda campaign in Spain, for instance, a Spaniard is the best person to organise it. Do you see what I'm getting at?'

'Noooo!' the crowd bellowed, enjoying themselves.

'We've always got our Ministry of Information, mate. Very helpful they are,' a man called out, laughing.

'The Ministry of Aggravation you mean – telling us what to do every five minutes,' a lady in an enormous black feathered hat shouted.

'Ministry of Misinformation, more like it – always gettin' it wrong!'

The crowd roared with laughter.

'That's exactly what I mean!' shouted Michael Foot, worried about losing his audience. 'Our propaganda is ineffective because nobody believes in it.' He had their attention again. 'Ladies and Gentlemen – there are Germans and Italians all over the world who believe in democracy just as we do. A man called Sebastian Haffner has written a book on Germany called *"Germany, Jekyll and Hyde"*. It's a brilliant analysis of the whole Nazi mind and make-up.'

'How's that gonna win us the war, mate?'

'Men like Haffner could help us with our propaganda. Did you know every German assault is preceded by a spate of rumours? German propagandists in every capital in the world are putting out rumours designed to confuse our people. Why don't we do the same?'

'How come you know so much about the Nazis?' a soldier asked from the back of the crowd.

Kate could feel waves of tension displace the crowd.

'Rob – let's go.'

'What?' He looked at her in astonishment; he was enjoying the argument.

'I've lived in Germany – I've read books,' the orator continued. 'Do you know what the Nazis do with the millions of alien peoples under their rule?'

'Kill 'em!' shouted a drunken old man with a carbuncle of a nose.

'Yes, they do kill some, but the majority are made to work for them. What do we do with alien brains in this country?'

'Pickle 'em?' bawled a blowzy woman, screaming with laughter as she hung onto the arm of the drunken old man for support.

'We waste them in internment camps, Madam, when we should be using them to help us.'

'How?' Rob called out.

The young man on the platform turned to Rob.

'How? By using their brains. We have experts in all sorts of important fields interned in camps. Scientists like Max Born, Rudolf Peierls, Hermann Bondi; doctors like Ludwig Gutmann; scholars like Ernst Gombrich and Niklaus Pevsner; psychologists like Hans Eysenck It's a scandalous waste of talent. And we could also use unskilled people to help us achieve victory by getting them to work in the factories and fields.'

'Fuckin' rubbish. How can you work next to a bleedin' Nazi or a Wop? They'd slit your throat as soon as look at you. Come back to real fuckin' world, mate.'

'Rob – can we go … please.' Kate hated this sort of heckling.

Rob reluctantly followed her, listening to the lines of rhetoric from the speakers.

'Invincible, that's what the British are and don't you forget it –'

'England, unlike Germany, has never tried to dominate another country –'

'"This is our finest hour," says Winny – so let's take pride in our country which has given so much to the ideas of politics and poetry in Europe –'

'The greatest terror is man, man in all his madness. There is never any justification for war. War is contrary to the Christian ethic. In trying to work out a philosophy of life I have discovered that all human life has a purpose, therefore all human life is precious, therefore all killing is sinful.'

'Crap! How can Hitler's life be precious, you bleedin' idiot?' shouted someone from the crowd.

'Bloody conchie!' shouted someone else.

A number of men started to push towards the speaker.

'Okay,' said Rob, guiding Kate out of the crowd. 'Let's go.'

They walked very fast from Speakers' Corner under a barrage of silver balloons hanging above their heads like swollen fish with outsize tails. A curious, almost melodic whine came from their cables moving in the light breeze. In the distance, a totally disparate scene: a corner of pre-war tranquillity – people boating and bathing at Lansbury's Lido. Heat and laughter shimmered off the water.

'I wish I had a bathing costume,' Kate said, looking enviously at people splashing in the Serpentine.

'I wish you had too.' Rob smiled down at her and Kate felt a tingling in her breasts.

She looked away from him to a kiosk. 'Shall we have a drink here?'

Rob bought them some Limeade and they sat silently in the sun to drink it.

Kate studied the relaxed holiday scene in front of them.

Rob looked at her. 'Penny for them.'

'Do you remember that cartoon in *The Standard* showing two old men tranquilly drinking beer in a pub and the caption read: "*Meanwhile, in Britain the entire population, faced by the threat of invasion has been flung into a state of complete panic.*" Bit like that, isn't it? Pity Goebbels can't see it.'

'He'd only reinvent it, Kate.'

'Oh God – why do we always talk about war?'

Rob looked at her in surprise 'I didn't know we did … what would you like to talk about?'

'Why was your last letter so cold?' She looked up at him quickly, noticing his eyes narrow.

'Was it?'

'You know it was. You usually write reams.'

Rob listened to the children screaming with delight as the water splashed over them.

'I did … in the first one … I didn't send it.'

'Why not?'

'I thought my CO would have a fit if he saw what I'd written about my German friend Axel.'

'I thought they didn't censor officers' letters.'

'Oh, don't you believe it. They often do.'

'Was that the only reason you didn't send it?'

Rob continued to look at the swimmers.

'Yes.'

A small silence.

'What else did you say?'

'Oh, just stuff about flying … you know. What do you want to do now?' he asked quickly.

'I thought we were going to the cinema.'

'If that's what you want.'

'Well that's what we decided, wasn't it? – the new Victoria.' She got up to go. 'At least *Wuthering Heights* isn't about war.'

No, Rob thought – just doomed love.

There was a queue at the Victoria Cinema. They joined it, staring, like everyone else in amazement at the colourful Art Deco interior. No one had seen anything like it before. A woman in the foyer summed it up for everyone. 'Hollywood has come to the West End, folks.'

There were posters of the beautiful Merle Oberon and Lawrence Olivier everywhere. Kate saw Rob staring at Merle Oberon's enormous blue eyes and wished she was that beautiful.

A couple of hours later, tears were streaming down Kate's face as Cathy lay dying and Heathcliff cried wildly over a surging background of music.

'*Do I want to live? What kind of living will it be when you – oh God! Would you like to live with your soul in the grave?'*

'Let me alone. Let me alone,' sobbed Catherine. *'If I've done wrong, I'm dying for it. It is enough. You left me too; but I won't unbraid you! I forgive you. Forgive me!'*

Then Heathciff carried the dying Cathy towards the window so she could see her moors once more.

There was a flutter of white handkerchiefs in the dark auditorium as women dabbed at eyes and blew noses.

Kate's eyes were still red when they were eating a meal in a crowded Lyons Corner House at Marble Arch. She was trying to listen to a small orchestra playing *The Rose of Trale*e in opposition to a thousand tongues of conversation.

'Good grief, Kate – it was melodramatic rubbish.' Rob ate a mouthful of food. 'Umm – it's good isn't it?'

Lyons, they'd discovered was serving roast pork and two vegetables, treacle pudding, bread and butter and coffee for only 11d. It had been worth the lengthy queuing, Rob thought.

'I loved it,' said Kate, 'and I know what you're going to say. It didn't follow the book and Olivier was a rotten Heathcliff.'

'Of course I am. Olivier's Heathciff would never be capable of beating his wife or murdering Hindley.'

'I don't think Heathcliff did kill Hindley – anyway I don't care what you say – I still loved it – all that swirling music and emotion.'

'But you spent most of the time crying through it, for God's sake.'

'That's what I enjoyed.'

'I'll never, never understand women.'

'Well, don't try then.' She put down her knife and fork. 'I can't eat any more.'

Kate looked around the enormous restaurant, heaving with service personnel and civilians. There were at least a thousand waitresses in smart black and white uniforms rushing around trying to serve everyone.

'Kate, what's wrong? You never used to bottle things up like this.'

'Me bottle things up? What about you?'

Rob carried on eating his meal.

'You see – you're doing it again.'

'What?'

'Not answering.'

'Why do you want to argue with me?'

'I don't … I want …'

'Yes?'

'I … don't know.'

'Are you having second thoughts about tonight?'

'No.' A slight pause. 'Yes.'

'Which is it?'

'I don't know.'

Rob stared at her. 'Look if you don't want to come – don't. I'm not going to force you.' Then he leaned across the table to hold her hand. 'Kate – we might not see each other again for months and months.'

He immediately hated himself as he saw the sudden fear in her eyes.

'Sorry – I shouldn't have said that.'

'No, it's true. We might never see each other again.'

Rob smiled. 'Oh God – you sound like Catherine Earnshaw.'

'But not as beautiful.'

'Oh yes – quite as beautiful.' And he leaned over the table and kissed her for a long time, while scores of shocked middle-aged men and women choked on their treacle pudding.

'It's on the top floor.'

Kate looked nervously around the room: two limp hand-towels hung on an ancient oak towel-rack by the hand basin; a bed by the window, covered with a faded blue counterpane; at the side of the bed, a small oak table and squatting on top of it, the most hideous object she had ever seen – a pink, china, hippopotamus yawning widely to receive cigarette ash.

The woman stared at her. Kate could feel her face flame with colour. Of course the woman knew.

'One night you say … £2 – in advance.'

'£2!'

Rob was about to argue when he saw Kate's face and gave the woman the money. He locked the door behind her.

'Well, she certainly saw us coming.'

'Perhaps it happens all the time … now there's a war on.' Kate walked over to the window and was just about to open the curtains when Rob yelled.

'The blackout!'

'Sorry – I forgot.'

He switched off the light and she threw back the curtains onto a full moon. She stared at a small, broken balcony outside their room. She didn't know what she was supposed to do.

Rob threw himself on the bed. The springs protested loudly. 'Bloody hell. She must have put us in here on purpose.'

He could see Kate silhouetted by the moonlight, unfamiliar in her WAAF uniform.

'Kate?'

'What?'

'Come here.'

She could only see a dark shape on the bed. It could be any man she thought.

'Don't you want to be here?'

'Of course I do… it's just…'

Silence was crushing them.

'Come here … please.' He held out his hand to her.

She walked over to him and he pulled her down onto the bed with him. The springs protested noisily as the bed yawned into a wide V.

'Oh, Christ.'

Their bodies rolled together. Kate could see liquid-dark eyes staring at her in the moonlight. And then Rob smiled, his familiar lop-sided smile and she was suddenly walking along a road after school when she was fourteen. Colin was walking on the opposite side when he suddenly spotted her and ran across. A tall good-looking boy strode effortlessly after him. She'd tried to dive into the house, thinking of her flat chest and spots, but Colin grabbed her arm.

'Hey – Kate – want to make up a foursome at tennis tonight with Rob and Angie White?'

Kate had gone scarlet, thinking her skin would look even worse now and stared down at the paving stones on the road.

'Can't – got homework.'

'God, you're boring. Come on Rob – we'll find another girl to make up the doubles with a bit more life in her.'

They'd swept past her up the road, then suddenly Rob had turned and smiled: a devastating lop-sided smile, and her heart had palpitated so badly she'd thought she was having a heart attack.

She could smell his body as he kissed her. She had always hated the smell of her brother's sweat so why didn't she mind Rob's? He touched her face with tentative fingers, almost as if he was reading her like Braille. And suddenly, she felt very calm; this was where she belonged. His fingers slid gently down her shirt; unbuttoning each button slowly as if he was practising a new skill. He moved back to look at her. She was wearing new silk underwear: pale blue, shimmering. She shivered as he removed her brassiere with one hand, more easily than she could have done. She tried to cover herself.

'No, don't – you look beautiful.'

He cupped each breast. 'I remember a time when you didn't have these.'

Her breath was a feather as his lips butterflied down her body. He flicked her nipples slowly with his tongue until the muscles in her stomach quivered.

She didn't know it would be like this. Didn't know her entire skin would flush with pleasure or feel her whole body opening to his touch. His tongue moved down her stomach and tendrils of fire licked between her legs.

'Oh, God,' she whispered, closing her eyes to shut out the world as he explored her.

A floorboard creaked. And again. Outside the room. The woman was listening on the other side of the door.

Kate shot up – her body a contradiction of disgust and excitement. The bed recoiled with a loud protest of springs.

'What do you want?' Rob shouted.

They heard soft footsteps retreat down the stairs. The sound of laughing people in the street outside.

He lay back on the bed; his face closed. A stranger.

Kate got up and walked to the window, hugging her body tight. She looked back at Rob who was staring out at the night-sky and suddenly noticed their uniforms in the moonlight, lying like weapons on a wooden chair.

Chapter 21

'Oh, the perfection of hindsight.'

James Carlisle.
The Feather Bed, 1906

By the time Rob returned to his squadron in 12 Group in the summer of 1940, Air-Marshall Dowding realised the odds against which his pilots were fighting. Gradually, throughout that summer, so did the pilots in all four Fighter Command groups. The Luftwaffe, they discovered, outnumbered them five to one.

By mid-July, the Germans had still not made a major assault against the British mainland; it was concentrating on sustained and fierce attacks on shipping in the Channel, hoping to disrupt or even halt the passage of convoys; at the same time they wanted to entice Dowding to release all his fighters into the action so that they could be annihilated. Dowding, against powerful opposition, refused. He only allowed Air Vice-Marshal Park, in charge of 11 Group, about 40% of the total force available, which created tremendous strain on the squadrons. Dowding thought that these attacks were only a foretaste of the real battle. He was right. Each day, exhausted British pilots returned from sorties with the Luftwaffe to reassemble at their dispersal points; waiting for a telephone call that would send many of them to an early grave; some of them without firing a tracer.

But not 12 Group. Not yet.

Rob's squadron had moved from Kirton-in-Lindsey, a bleak, windswept airfield north of Lincoln, to Manston, a big grass airfield on the eastern tip of Kent for their annual summer camp. They were living in tents dotted around the airfield. Rob could see Colin and the others in the distance as the truck drove over the grass towards them. They all waved.

The pilots had been lounging in the sun as they waited for Rob to arrive. Colin ran towards the truck as Rob got out, his smiling sun-raw face covered with enormous freckles.

'Christ – you skinny bastard.' He gave Rob a bear hug. 'You've obviously missed our haute cuisine.'

'How d'you put on weight with RAF food, Col?' Rob asked him, laughing. They all milled around him. Tall 'Cocky' Dumas with his crooked teeth and engaging conversation, 'Butch' Morton who flew so close in formation you felt he was breathing on your neck, even the paradoxical 'B' flight Commander, Colin Macfie – very good-looking, exceptionally shy and eccentric, wearing as usual, a long tartan scarf draped around his neck in the heat.

Colin's hand swept around the field. 'Welcome to Manston – gateway to France. After Hawarden and Mud! After Kirton and Wind! Comes!' Colin made trumpet noises. 'Manston and Sun … Think things are looking up, Robbie boy.'

But Rob wasn't listening, he was staring at a Spitfire Mark 1 standing at the edge of the field. Someone had painted the word *Sirius* on the side of it. He let out a whoop of joy as he ran across to it.

'Who says she's yours, you skinny bastard,' Colin shouted after him, a broad grin on his good-natured face. 'You've got impeccable timing, Robert – there's a Mess dinner tonight. Oh, by the way,' he added casually, 'you've been made a Flying Officer.'

Rob had arrived in time for an inspection from the Air Officer Commanding No. 12 Fighter Group, Air Vice-Marshall Leigh-Mallory. A dinner party had been arranged in his honour in the Mess tent. It was a drunken affair.

'They're obviously celebrating my promotion, Col,' said Rob, toasting himself again.

'Yeah – nothing to do with old mournful Mallory … Cheers.' Colin knocked back another glass of port.

They started the after-dinner games at 22.00 hours. Rob climbed up the pole in the middle of the tent, shouting for Mallory to follow him and squeezed through one of the ventilation flaps near the top. They heard him clamber over the ridge pole and suddenly his head popped through another ventilation flap at the other end of the tent. They watched him slide expertly down another pole. Everyone cheered, even the Air Vice-Marshall. A queue of energetic, slim pilots followed his example.

'Come on, Col – you fat bastard – you next,' Rob shouted out drunkenly. 'Not chicken are you?'

Colin walked towards Rob and poured some port over his head before finishing off another glass.

Suddenly, the thickened figure of Leigh-Mallory got up, swaying with the effects of the fine port he'd consumed, and to everyone's surprise started to climb the pole. They all began chanting. 'Mall-o-ry. Mall-o-ry. Mall-or-y.' A cheer resounded round the tent as he reached the top, his head disappearing through the ventilation flap. They watched his large buttocks and legs wriggling desperately to free themselves. A number of pilots climbed onto the table and shoved him through the flap. They roared with laughter as they watched the dent of his progress along the top of now dangerously sagging tent. Four of them raced outside to follow the action, and found Colin lying on the grass staring up at the sky.

'I may be in the gutter,' he shouted, 'but I have my eyes on the – Jesus Christ!'

Leigh-Mallory, purple with exertion, slid down the side of the collapsing tent onto Colin's chest.

Rob rushed to drag the Air Vice-Marshall off him.

'Are you all right, Sir?'

'Is *he* all right!' Colin gasped, holding his chest. 'That's bloody rich. I think he's broken my ribs!'

Leigh-Mallory peered down at Colin before straightening his uniform and dignity. He leaned forward, breathing port into Rob's startled mouth.

'I never forget faces, young man.' Then he weaved off into the darkness.

The other pilots shook their heads at Rob and Colin in mock horror.

'Short career in the RAF, was it, old chaps?'

'Oh dear ... oh dear... glad I didn't man-handle the old boy.'

'I never forget faces, young man,' they chorused in Mallory's sonorous tones as they staggered back into the tent.

Two weeks after the incident with Leigh-Mallory, Rob and Colin were posted to No. 19 Squadron in Fowlmere: a satellite station of Duxford in Cambridgeshire.

'Pure coincidence?' said Colin.

'I can't believe it, Col – it's a famous squadron.'

'What for – killing Germans or us?'

Rob saw his first sight of the new cannon-armed Spitfires, the Spitfire, Mk1B. The specially shaped wings had a huge blister on top for the magazine. It was armed with two 20 mm Hispano cannon and four .303 inch machine-guns. Not many had been delivered so far and Rob was desperate to have one.

They had been told to report to A Flight hut on the northernmost tip of the airfield. As they opened the door they were faced with the picture of a naked woman on the wall. Underneath her, a wag had written: *Time spent on reconnaissance is never wasted.*

They looked at each other and laughed.

'I'm definitely going to like it here,' Colin said as Squadron Leader Pinkham walked into the room.

'Adams and Brazier?'

'Yes, Sir.' They both saluted.

'Good. Just in time for the lecture. Follow me.' He walked off rapidly in the direction of another hut.

'Of course … you may be wrong, Col.'

After the usual introductions to the other pilots, their new Squadron Leader, Tommy Pinkham, gave them a lecture on the merits and demerits of the cannon.

'Okay – I know you're all desperate to get your hands on the new cannon Spits, but before you do, the disadvantages – stoppages are too frequent and stoppages on one cannon make it very difficult to keep a steady sight with the other. Also the firing period is restricted to six seconds making defence against other fighter aircraft very difficult.'

'Then what the hell have we got them for?' someone shouted out.

'Advantages.' Pinkham continued smoothly. 'It has terrific destructive power and we need that power.' He paused. 'The Germans are now armour-plating their aircraft.'

The pilots looked at each other. Most of their planes weren't.

'The cannon also has high muzzle velocity which decreases the amount of deflection necessary in deflection shooting and increases range and accuracy … Does that answer your question?' Pinkham said, looking at the pilot who'd been sceptical.

The next day all the pilots found themselves on a training programme designed to test the new systems of attack that

Pinkham had developed to cope with the disadvantages, and make full use of the advantages of the new armament.

Rob was in *A* flight with 'Sandy' Lane as his Flight Commander. They dived in echelon from 2,000 ft above and to the side of their target aircraft to dead astern, closed rapidly, and gained a very steady sight for the two cannon at high speed. The break-away was carried out downwards and to the side. Attack was then renewed from above and to the side again. The big advantage Pinkham had told them: German bombers tended to fly just beneath cloud base. B flight continued these practices in the afternoon and the new squadron formations were posted up in diagrammatic form in the dispersal hut. Being based on sections of two aircraft in line astern, it was highly manoeuvrable.

A week later, Rob and eleven other Spitfire pilots were scrambled and ordered to patrol Duxford at 20,000 ft, then vectored southeast to cover Debden. The R/T abruptly burst into life.

'Bandits – 100+. Angels 15!'

And suddenly the sky was full of what looked like black bees. Approaching the twelve small Spitfires was a formation of Do 17Z bombers, escorted by Me 110s and 109s fighters.

Rob felt his heart thump against his ribs as he saw a second formation: fifty more bombers and fighters were behind them. Christ.

'Line Astern – Go!' shouted 'Sandy' over the R/T.

And they went into attack using the two aircraft in line-astern formation they had been practising.

Twelve Spitfires against a hundred enemy planes.

It was a disaster.

They discovered to their horror that the cannon would only hit the target if they were flying absolutely straight and level, but worse even than this, was the problem with the belt-feed mechanism which fed bullets into the breech – it jammed whenever the pilots applied any gee.

'Yellow Two – Break!'

A Messerschmitt was on Rob's tail. He swerved violently and orange tracers shot through the space he'd just vacated. His finger futilely pressed the firing button. His cannon had jammed three times already.

His hands were slippery with sweat as he fought to keep the Spitfire turning in tight circles; the one manoeuvre that the Messerschmitt couldn't follow. He swerved frantically as a Spitfire, trailing smoke, flew diagonally in front of him. Then suddenly, without warning, the German planes disappeared – obviously ordered back into formation to attack their original target. Rob was left with a sick feeling in his stomach and a violent need to urinate.

Half an hour later, when he walked into the dispersal hut, Squadron Leader Pinkham was pacing up and down: his face dark red with bottled anger.

'If those Messerschmitts hadn't had orders to stay close to the Dorniers we'd all be bloody dead.' He looked at Rob. 'Lawson and Clouston are back. Any sign of the others?'

Rob sat down suddenly, shaking from delayed shock.

'Saw a couple bale out.'

They suddenly heard the sound of a returning Spitfire over the airfield, but the noise of the engine was too high. They rushed outside to see PO Aerberhardt's Spitfire diving towards the airfield, trailing smoke. Rob watched in horror as the plane exploded into the field and burst into flames. The pilot was nineteen. He heard the clanging bells of the fire-engine and ambulance as they bounced over the field. Everyone on the airfield ran towards the blazing funeral pyre. Rob watched medical orderlies kicking smoking pieces of metal aside in search of human remains and suddenly the smell of burning flesh flamed in Rob's nostrils. He was sick over his flying boots.

Pinkham walked casually over to him. 'Time for a shower and a drink, Rob.' He pushed him towards the Mess.

That night Pinkham wrote a furious letter to Fighter Command stating why the cannon Spitfires needed to be immediately re-equipped with the old machine-guns before he lost all his fighter pilots. Subsequently, the cannon Spitfires were replaced by Spitfire Mk 1A from no. 7 Operational Training Unit at Hawarden. Dowding himself had authorized the urgent replacements.

Yet weeks later, Rob's squadron found themselves at the centre of another battle; this time an internal one over tactics. Douglas Bader, the legendary pilot who had lost his legs eight years earlier, but had talked himself back into flying, had become the CO of 202 squadron. He wanted to develop the 'Wing Concept'; whereby a number of squadrons flew together as a cohesive unit. Leigh-Mallory had listened to Bader's ideas, liked them, and thus the Duxford Wing was born.

Bader advocated far more aggressive tactics than were practised by Fighter Command. He believed in attack with surprise from the sun and swooping from height, not letting the bombers become aware of a whole squadron queuing up. An attacker pressing close from a surprise attack had little to fear, he said, for the deflection problems for a bomber's gunners became acute the closer the attack, while the fighter pilot had an engine and an armoured windscreen in front of him.

Colin was overawed by Bader's square-jawed confidence, but Rob, whilst agreeing with his tactics, had reservations: both about the Big Wing Concept and the man himself, especially after what Sergeant Unwin had told him. Unwin had been a clerk in Uxbridge on first joining the RAF and had read reports concerning a court of enquiry about a flying accident in which Bader was involved. It stated that Bader had been drunk and flying too low; he had gone into a roll at 50 feet and his Spitfire had crashed. His legs had had to be amputated, but he had survived. However, once Bader was well enough to testify, none of his evidence tied in with the report. Three other officers had been involved in similar incidents and were court-martialled, but not Bader. Later, when Unwin had become a Flight Sergeant, he had, coincidentally, been posted to Bader's squadron and flew as his number two. One day, he told Rob, he'd seen Bader crash his Spitfire on take-off because he'd forgotten to put it into fine pitch and had smashed his artificial legs. Rob looked at him in the Mess one day surrounded by a crowd of admiring young pilots and wondered if courage was merely another name for perversity.

The pilots of 242, 310 and 19 squadrons were all sitting in a lecture hall at Duxford waiting for Bader to give them a lecture on Big Wing tactics before their first sortie. He suddenly stomped in and walked noisily up the Hall while everyone fell silent.

The confident features of a man who knows his own worth faced them.

'The Big Wing, gentlemen.' Bader looked around at the sea of young faces in front of him. 'The concept behind the Big Wing is simple.' They could all hear his legs squeak as he paced up and down. '242 & 310 Hurricane squadrons will climb to 20,000 feet, their best operating height, while No 19 Spitfire squadron will be positioned 4,000 to 5,000 feet above, to tackle the Me109s, thus freeing the Hurricanes to attack the bombers. The Hurricane squadrons will take off from Duxford at the same time as No 19 Squadron take off from Fowlmere. There will be no joining up over the airfield. You'll fly straight on course and climb quickly while the other squadrons take up their positions.

The Hurricanes will fly in line astern together, while the Spits will fly above, behind and to one side. The idea being that the Spitfire, with their better performance –'

Bader paused as the usual bantering between the Hurricane and Spitfire pilots had its place, then raised his hand quickly for silence.

'But of course, gentlemen, only in climbing to an altitude of 20,000 ft in thirteen minutes – nothing else.'

He paused again while everyone laughed.

'The Spits will guard the Hurricanes against interference by Messerschmitt 109s, while the latter attack the enemy formation. If there are no enemy fighters, gentlemen, the Spits will come down on the bombers after the Hurricanes have broken them up … Any questions?'

While Bader answered questions from the pilots, Rob was thinking of the highly effective Jagdgeschwader formation the Germans had used in the Spanish Civil War – four planes with two leaders and two wing-men to protect them. Why on earth couldn't the British learn something from the Germans with their experience of fighting in Spain? Rob felt his mouth become very dry as he stood up. He was going to ask Bader why he didn't think of employing German tactics. Suddenly everyone else in the room stood up too as Bader stomped out of the Hall with Air Vice-Marshall Leigh-Mallory in tow. The lecture had ended. Rob swore to himself.

'Bader's ideas are great – in theory,' he heard FO Frank Brinsen saying to Colin as he walked into the Mess later. 'But what happens if we're attacked before we've got into position?'

'We'll be a pretty formidable force,' Colin argued. 'It could deter the Krauts from attacking at all.'

'Oh, come on!' said Rob, joining them. 'How much manoeuvrability are we going to lose if we're flying in tight formation? – and how the hell can we continually change altitude to avoid ack-ack fire?'

'Well, we'll break up when we engage, won't we?'

'Then what's the bloody point of the Big Wing?' Rob asked.

'Numbers, old boy,' said Frank, looking around for a drink. 'Frighten the Hun into submission.'

'I wonder how old Tommy is going to react.'

As if on cue the Squadron Leader walked into the Mess and they called him over. He didn't look pleased.

'What do you think, Tommy?' Rob asked him.

'It's academic what I think – it's a fait accompli. Bader's got the go-ahead … I'm going to get a drink.' They watched him walk over to a fellow officer who was organising the bar.

'Well, that says it all,' said Frank, leaning over conspiratorially towards them. 'I think we're in for a rough ride, chaps. Anyway – tomorrow's another day. Who's for a drink?'

The next day the Duxford Wing took off, passing the machine-gun post, manned by steel-helmeted aircraftmen in the middle of the airfield, to patrol the London area. There were two Hurricane squadrons in a wedge below, the Spits above and to one side.

Rob looked out of his cockpit. In front of him was Flight Lieutenant Sandy Lane leading the red section. Thank God I'm in his section, he thought. Sandy was a pilot of exceptional ability. As they were climbing away to the south, Bader's voice rang out on R/T.

'Dogsbody calling, Woody. Over.'

'Woody' was Woody Woodall, the Controller of Duxford. He had the cool, unruffled ability to size up a situation presented to him on the big board in his operations room and then to give directions to his pilots in a voice which invariably remained calm, even at times of immense stress.

'Controller here, Dogsbody. Loud and Clear. Over.'

'Woody, do me a favour, would you, old boy? Ring up Buster Chinford and tell him I'm on for squash tomorrow. 09.30 hours. Over.'

There was a short silence before Rob heard 'Woody' agree.

Jesus Christ, he thought.

They had been flying only a few minutes when the R/T burst into life again.

'Hallo, Dogsbody. 100 plus bandits approaching. Vector 120 degrees. Angels 20. Buster. Over.'

And suddenly the sky was full of German aircraft: eighty bombers, Heinkel He111s and Dornier 17s, flying in fourteen tight double 'Vics' of six. The 'Vics' were stepped from 12,000 feet to 14,000 feet. Behind and above the bombers, Rob saw about thirty twin-engine Bf110 fighter escorts, stepped from 15,000 to 20,000 feet.

'Climb! Climb! Climb!' Bader shouted over the R/T.

They hadn't had time to get to the right height.

Rob climbed to 25,000 feet and saw a yellow-nosed Me109 passing over his head flying south-southeast. He continued to climb fast and chased it, firing a short burst into the side of the Me. A large section tore off its starboard wing and the starboard engine streamed glycol as it went down. Another Messerschmitt on his port-side was following the almost standardized method of evasion – a half roll, followed by a vertical dive down to the ground. Rob anticipated the actions and dived after it firing his machine guns. He saw the bullets rake the side of the plane before he pulled up sharply out of the dive. Two hits! Unbelievable.

'Red Section. Line astern,' Sandy called over the R/T.

Three Spitfires were about to fight twenty Dorniers: Sandy – Red one, Rob – Red two, Colin – Red three. They flew in line astern, heading straight for the Dorniers when suddenly Sandy dropped the nose of his Spitfire. Rob and Colin briefly followed suit before they all suddenly hauled back hard on their control sticks as Sandy led them into a steep climb turning to the left. In two seconds the Germans had lost their advantage. They were above them. Sandy fired a short burst of fire at the leading plane; the Dornier went into the expected half-roll. Rob was certain it was his. He kicked the rudder automatically to the left, to fix the plane at right angles. He knew where the Dornier would be when he pressed the gun button. He saw the tracers from the Brownings thud into his target before a jet of flames shot upwards. The Dornier spun out of sight.

Three hits! The adrenalin pumped round Rob's body.

Suddenly, the sky was an explosion of weaving planes and parachutes. Too many Spitfires and Messerschmitts in the same air space – no coordination, no sequence. Rob had to focus all his mind on avoiding collision. The air was full of smoke and tracers as the planes whirled around in desperate efforts to shoot each other and to avoid being shot.

He was a mixture of terror and ecstasy as he weaved in and out of planes, taking 'shots' whenever an enemy became a momentary target.

In his rear-view mirror, he suddenly saw a yellow-nosed Me shoot out golden rain and a cannon shell exploded inside his Spitfire. He instinctively turned on his back and the Spit went into a vertical dive. Panic lacerated his body.

The cabin was so full of smoke that he couldn't even see the instruments. He forgot everything he'd been told about fire: unfasten your harness – unplug your oxygen and radio before you open your canopy to bale out – the extreme draught will bring in the flames that cause the smoke. He tore at the canopy to be able to see. It jammed. He could feel the terror rising in his throat and a great scream erupted in the cabin as he tore at the canopy with both hands. It suddenly shot back and the smoke cleared instantly as if he'd recited a magic formulae. He pulled back on the stick bringing the Spit out of the dive, taking great gulps of air.

His hands were shaking as he looked out of the open canopy: a machine-gun pane was missing from his starboard wing, a shell had exploded inside it, and there was a bullet hole in the top of the engine cover. That seemed to be all the structural damage. But the engine sounded like a cement mixer. Rob throttled back quickly and looked at the engine instruments. The radiator temperature needle was jammed against its upper stop and so was the oil temperature indicator. The oil pressure needle had disappeared below the scale.

Rob realised that the damage to the radiator had lost him all his glycol coolant. That's why he had smoke, he thought. He suddenly remembered it had been white.

He kept taking deep breaths, making his brain think logically again. He had to fly over the Channel; at least if he ditched there he would have a chance of being picked up by the Sea Rescue Patrol.

He changed to coarse pitch, thinking this would help the propeller nurse the engine. It now sounded terminal.

Oh, Christ! No!

Out of nowhere, a lone Me109 came up behind him. He went again into the defensive circle, the engine protesting. Black smoke now pouring out of his exhaust.

He could feel his body quiver with the strain as the Me followed him round and round. He knew he couldn't carry on much longer.

Then suddenly the Me broke away sharply, waggled its wings, and disappeared into cloud. Rob was alone. His stunned brain tried to comprehend an act of chivalry in wartime. The Messerschmitt pilot could have shot him at any time.

He set course for England, never thinking he would reach it, but he hadn't calculated on the wonders of the Merlin engine; although it was near red-heat, it kept going, not merely as far as the Channel, but clear across to Hawkinge, the emergency aerodrome.

Rob's circuit drew the attention of the whole aerodrome. He didn't know that the cannon shell in his right wing had blown the tyre to pieces; he just felt the landing in a series of grotesque kangaroo hops along the airfield which finished in a wide loop. He was too exhausted to move when the Spitfire came to a halt. Two of the aircrew helped him out of the cockpit. He slid down the wing and collapsed on the grassy airfield.

Chapter 22

'The bitter grief of
leaving is like the spring grass;
however far you go you find it growing there.'

P'ing Li Yu (937-975)
Chinese Poet

'Do you think we'll be sent away soon, Miss?' Rose asked Sara.

Sara knew the children had been reading the local paper to see if they were going to be evacuated. All the teachers had been told in advance that they were. She felt incredibly sad to think that she wouldn't be teaching her class any more, but proud that so many of them had passed their 11 + examination. But not Charlie. She remembered the closed expression on his face when she'd told him. If only she'd had more time with him, he would have passed easily. She looked around the classroom, took a deep breath and kept her voice light.

'Yes, I think so, Rose.'

A range of emotions could be seen on the children's faces: fear, nervousness, even excitement on Carole's, but on Charlie's – nothing. Nothing at all. Sara wondered if he'd been listening.

'You'll meet the teachers who'll be travelling with you next week and they'll help to settle you into your new homes in Hertfordshire. And Charlie can tell you what it's like to be evacuated, can't you, Charlie?'

He didn't answer, but stared out of the window.

Sara was disturbed by his calm.

'Charlie?'

'Yeah?'

'Did you hear what I said?'

'Yeah.'

'Well?'

'Well, what?'

It was as if the clock had been turned back a year and she was facing the enemy in the form of a small Cockney child who'd just arrived in Hastings.

'Could you tell the class what it's like to be evacuated?'

There was a long silence before Charlie turned a perfectly impassive face towards Sara.

'No,' he said.

Hilda looked out of the scullery window onto the green jungle of her garden, sun-baked, humming with insects. Curtains of gnats rose and descended as if on invisible wires as she watched them. No one to tend the garden now she was busy at the WVS and Bill had to attend all these civil defence meetings. Wouldn't even talk about them. As if she was going to tell anyone secrets.

A blaze of butterflies: blues, tortoiseshells, peacocks and admirals, flitted in and out of the jungle of weeds and flowers. She'd always loved their lightness; their delicacy. She looked down at her ample body; she'd been light and delicate once too, before the children. She put Rose's wet, white dress through the new *ACME* wringer Colin had bought her. Colin. She sighed as she thought of him. Only three visits in four months, and each time he left she thought her heart would break.

And now Rose was leaving too. Stop it! Remember the results.

All three of her children passing for the grammar school. Hilda thought her head would explode with pride. Even though it had cost Bill and her so much money in uniforms and books, it had been worth it. They had something she had never had.

Education. She remembered all the time she'd spent at home looking after a sick mother when she should have been in school. Her father hadn't been able to cope with two little girls after his wife had died. So she had learned to be a mother at ten and was in service at thirteen.

She walked out into the sunshine, watching the butterflies flutter away as she pegged out the wash. At least Rose would go away with dazzlingly white clothes – they'd been soaking in Reckitt's Blue for hours. Her hands shook as she pegged the last item – Rose's old Teddy. She had made him for Rose when she was four. His large, brown, smiling face with its wet fur stared back at Hilda from the washing line. Rose had wanted him to look smart for the journey.

Her mouth quivered as she thought of their conversation yesterday when she'd told Rose about the new film in the *Gaiety*.

'*The Wizard of Oz*, Mum? – you're not serious? … that's so childish. I want to see *The Man in The Iron Mask*. That's exciting.'

Of course Hilda knew why she was so keen on that film, Charlie had read the book. Such a contradiction of a child, Hilda thought, and suddenly realised with a shock that the war had turned her into a contradiction too.

The bus was late, so they arrived at the *Gaiety* just as the lights were dimming. Mary and Charlie were waiting for them in row M. They squeezed quickly along the row of people to sit next to them just as the film started. Hilda looked around at the packed auditorium; people were going to the cinema two or even three times a week now, to get away from the war. She felt a lump in the throat as she recalled taking her younger sister to the *Central Picture Theatre* in Station Road. She'd got her first month's wages as a kitchen-maid and paid 6d each for the best seats. A fortune in those days. But worth every penny to see

Jeanie's little face light up when she heard the pianist, Mrs Collins, playing some lively music as Charlie Chaplin walked out with his sweetheart. Hilda remembered the ornate gas-lamps covered with red shades brightening up the walls during the interval when they were served with free tea and biscuits. And the sound-effects man had made them laugh, sitting on a chair by the screen, clacking coconuts when cowboys had rushed across the Prairie. Nothing like that these days.

'Do you feel like a walk, Mary,' said Hilda after they had left the cinema. 'I'd like a chat.'

Mary looked at her quickly. 'So would I.'

They watched the children walking ahead of them down the Queen's Road towards the Albert Memorial.

'Have you noticed they don't seem to run about like they used to?' Hilda said.

'Charlie doesn't do a lot of things he used to. Doesn't talk to us much any more.'

'Doesn't he?' Hilda looked at Mary in amazement. Rose was always telling her how Charlie answered all the questions in class. 'Was he very upset about not passing his 11+?'

'He must have been – but he's never mentioned it to us. Not once. I wish Rob had been home when we had the results.'

The women wandered across the road towards the sea front, looking at the children.

'Rose has become so pretty this last year, Hilda.'

'She hasn't been a nuisance, has she, Mary? Always at your house these days.'

'No, it's been lovely to have a girl in the house … you must be very proud of her.'

Hilda beamed. 'Oh I am and not just because she passed the exam … you know.'

'You're so lucky having a son and two daughters.'

Hilda turned to Mary in surprise. She sounded as if she envied her. Her – plain Hilda Brazier. When Mary had everything – money, looks and confidence.

'You never wanted any more children after Rob?'

There was a long silence as they walked through the beautiful evening, filled with sea-washed light. 'Sorry – I shouldn't have asked, Mary – you must think me –'

'No, it's all right … it's just … I've never spoken about it before … not to anyone.'

Hilda looked at the pain on Mary's face and could have bitten her tongue off.

'Two years after Rob was born I had twin girls … they both died.'

'Oh, my dear, I'm so sorry.'

'They died on the 24th December, 1921 at 2.30 in the afternoon. It was snowing outside. I remember thinking, how could snow be falling out of the sky when my babies had just died of diphtheria? They only lived for two months. John was more devastated than me at first – he'd always wanted a daughter you see. And I had given him two … and then they died and I found out … I couldn't have any more.'

'Oh, Mary – I … don't know what to say. All these years – not telling any one.'

'There wasn't any one to tell. John and I are both only children. Brought up to be "stoic in the face of adversity". Only I wasn't … it seemed like the end of the world.'

'But you had Rob.'

'Oh, yes, I had Rob. If I hadn't, I wouldn't be here.'

They walked in silence for some time before Mary turned to Hilda. 'I … went into Hellingly … the mental hospital … for … for over six months. I just couldn't seem to get over it, you see … John had to get a nurse to look after Rob.'

Hilda felt quite faint and clutched Mary's arm.

'What's the matter?'

She suddenly gave a great whoop of laughter. Mary looked at her in distress.

'Why are you laughing?'

'Oh, the relief, Mary … I could dance along the sea front.' She stopped laughing as she saw the distress on Mary's face. 'Oh, I'm not laughing because you went into Hellingly, dear. I'm laughing because I've been in and out of there like a dose of salts. They told me it was nervous breakdowns, but I don't know. I've thought I was completely mad so many times … You can't imagine the relief, Mary – knowing that you've been in there too.' She laughed again. 'That's not what I mean – you know that. But if you've been there – you, so calm and controlled – there's hope for me then, isn't there?'

Hilda beamed as Mary put her arms around her.

Charlie and Rose were standing by Hastings Pier, waiting for Mary and Hilda to catch them up when they saw a squad of soldiers crawling all over it.

'What do you think they're doing, Charlie?'

'Dunno. Smashing it up I expect, like everything else in the town.'

Rose looked at him. He wasn't the same Charlie any more and she didn't know how to get the old one back.

'What would they want to do that for?'

He shrugged his shoulders.

'Charlie … I'm frightened about going away … I've never been away from home before without my Mum.'

He picked up a big stick and threw it in an arc above the barbed wire towards the sea. It somersaulted over a rock.

'What's it like?'

But Charlie was staring at the soldiers who seemed to be cutting the pier into two.

'What?'

'What's it like living away from home?'

He turned to look at Rose. 'Depends.'

'On what?'

'On what your home's like.'

Charlie's eyes followed a pipe running under the pier into a tunnel under the road. He walked across the road up towards the White Rock Gardens trying to imagine where the pipe was going. When he reached the top he saw the pipe divide and disappear into two hideously ugly oil tanks right next to the colourful floral clock.

'Where's Charlie?'

Rose was still standing at the entrance of the pier as Hilda and Mary walked up to her.

'He's over there.' Rose pointed to the gardens. 'He wants to find out what the pipe's for.'

Hilda and Mary looked at the demolition work on the pier.

'Good God – what are they doing?' Hilda marched onto the pier. Mary and Rose saw her waving her arms angrily at the soldiers, pointing at the chaos they were creating.

She marched back towards them, her face flushed with anger.

'They're only going to break the pier into two sections with some bombs – and not only this one, but ours at St Leonards as well – to stop the Nazis from using it as a landing base. That corporal told me. I could kill Hitler with my own bare hands. Our lovely piers.' Hilda's face was contorted with emotion.

Rose looked at her mother nervously.

'You all right, Mum?'

'And up there –' Hilda pointed to where Charlie was standing, '– they've got ruddy great oil tanks. If the Hun come here they're going to release the oil and set light to it and …' She suddenly started shaking and great sobs tore out of her.

Rose rushed up to her mother and put her arms around her. 'It'll be all right, Mum. They won't land here, will they, Mrs Adams? They'll go to Dover – it's nearer.'

Hilda tried every night not to think about Rose going away and every night she failed. Every night she lay at the side of her snoring husband and stared at the discoloured ceiling in their bedroom. After four days she looked haggard. She could see it in the eyes of the women at the WVS centre. All of them so kind and no one understanding. She got through each day by working until she thought she would drop from exhaustion. But she didn't.

And then it came. The day the children were leaving.

The authorities didn't want the parents to come to the station. Congestion they said. Say goodbye at the school. Less upsetting all round. Hilda had a numb feeling in her limbs as she walked with Rose to the school; Rose's hand tightly clenched in hers. Her suitcase was neatly packed with everything Hilda could put in it. She had to have light clothes for the summer and a few warm things ... just in case. It was a bright, clear morning. Not a cloud in the sky and Hilda couldn't feel her limbs.

The school yard was full of noise when they arrived. Hundreds of children milling round with small cases, excitement and fear on their faces. An army of teachers were putting labels on them. Rose's hand was still tightly clenched in Hilda's. She saw Mary in the distance with Charlie. Thank God.

Charlie was looking up at the sky as if waiting for Rob to parachute into the school yard at any moment. Hilda almost ran over to them.

'Well, here we are then, Mary.'

Mary gave Hilda a small smile which didn't reach her eyes.

A teacher near them with a large sheet of paper started calling out names and children were marshalled into small groups. Hilda felt Rose's hand tighten in hers.

'Charles Adams,' the woman called out. Charlie looked at Mary who nodded to him. He walked over to a group of children on the far side of the yard. The teacher continued down the list.

'I thought it would be easier for Charlie if he went in our name,' Mary whispered, almost apologetically to Hilda.

'They're calling the children's names alphabetically – wouldn't it be wonderful if they put Rose in the same group as Charlie?'

'Rose Brazier,' the teacher shouted. Another teacher came and took Rose away from her mother towards Charlie's group. Hilda could still feel the pressure of Rose's fingers on her palm.

'Thank God they're together, Mary.'

Rose stood close to Charlie who was still staring up at the sky.

'Hilda – I'm really worried about him.'

'Of course you are – I'm worried to death about Rose leaving too.'

'No, it's more than that … Look at him.'

Hilda did look at him. All the other children were waving, smiling or simply staring at their parents. Charlie, alone, ignored everything that was going on. He wasn't there, she thought with a shock.

'You wouldn't believe the change in him. He barely said goodbye to John this morning – just walked past him down the hall.'

Hilda put her arm around Mary's shoulder.

'He'll be all right, dear, once he's settled in. He's nervous of change, that's all. It just comes out a different way with a boy – girls get clingy.'

'Perhaps we could go up to Hertfordshire together next month to see them, Hilda? What do you think?'

Hilda didn't know what to say. Where would she get the money for the train fare from?

'But perhaps Charlie wouldn't want to see me.' Mary had the same knot in her stomach as she'd had on her first day at school. Charlie hadn't looked in her direction once.

'Don't be daft – course he will,' Hilda said.

The teacher shouted out to the parents again. 'We'll be leaving in a few minutes for the station. Could parents say goodbye now, please. We've still got a lot of organising to do.'

There was a hurl of bodies as parents and children ran towards each other for a final kiss and hug. Charlie stood still as Mary walked towards him.

'Aren't I going to get a kiss, Charlie?' Mary's eyes shone with tears as she looked down into his impassive face.

'Yeah.' He reached up and pecked Mary's cheek. She could see Hilda and Rose locked in a silent embrace: tears running down both their cheeks.

'Charlie,' Hilda called. Charlie and Mary walked over to them. 'Can I ask you something?'

He nodded.

'Will you promise to look after my Rose for me? She's never …' Hilda's mouth started quivering.

Charlie looked from Hilda's tearful face to Rose's and nodded again.

'No, say you promise, Charlie.'

'All right – I promise.' Charlie's voice was impersonal.

'A solemn promise, Charlie?' Mary looked deep into Charlie's hazel eyes and he looked back at her for the first time in weeks. A flicker of pain passed momentarily along his face before his features became a mask once more.

'Like the solemn promise I gave you, Auntie Mary?'

Mary felt the shock all down her back. Then suddenly the children were whisked away and the women were left stranded on the empty asphalt school-yard.

The children left Hastings at eight o'clock in the morning. It was six p.m. by the time they arrived in Benington, near Stevenage in Hertfordshire, and were taken to the tiny village hall, swaying with exhaustion.

The hall was full of adults waiting to collect their new foster children. It was organised differently from Charlie's last evacuation. This time people just shouted out names and children just went with whoever called out their name. There was hardly any noise from the children.

'I want to go to the same house as you, Charlie,' whispered Rose, very close to tears.

Charlie went up to one of the teachers.

'Can me and Rose stay together?'

The teacher looked harassed. This was the culmination of weeks of organisation and she was as exhausted as the children. She looked at his label. 'You're Dr. Adams' son, aren't you?'

'Yeah,' said Charlie, not looking at the woman.

'I'll see what I can do.' She walked off to talk to some of the other teachers, then came back.

'I'm sorry, Charlie – all the billets have been organised already. There can't be any changes.'

Rose suddenly burst into tears and an old lady came up to her and gave her a biscuit. 'Now don't you be crying, little 'un, you'll like it here, we're a friendly lot.'

'Rose Brazier,' a tremulous voice called out.

Rose froze. Two elderly ladies, both wearing stiff black dresses, looked around the room.

'Oh, Charlie.' Rose couldn't move her legs.

'Rose Brazier,' the elderly voice quivered again.

'It's all right, Rose. I'll find out where you're living. Go on. They look all right – bit old, but that don't matter.'

Rose moved towards the old women, her suitcase tight in her hand. She turned back to Charlie. He waved her forward.

Charlie watched the hall emptying the same as last time and stood rigidly in a corner of the room, which smelt of moth balls and old musty wood. A short man, about fifty, with thinning grey hair and startlingly bushy black eyebrows walked quickly into the room to speak to one of the teachers. She pointed at Charlie. The man smiled as he walked towards him. He looked as if he didn't have a neck at all, Charlie thought; his heavy jaw rose out from broad shoulders in a single column. As he got nearer, a smell hit Charlie full in the face. He didn't know what it was then, but he learned in the following weeks. Manure.

'Sorry I'm late, young 'un – work on the farm.' He stuck out a large calloused arm and Charlie saw thick dark hair sprouting out of the cuffs of his flannel shirt.

There was something about the man that made Charlie stick his hand out too; he felt his knuckles being squeezed together in a powerful grip.

'Bert Ackroyd – you'll be Charlie Adams – a doctor's son I've been told. You'll find it a bit different from home I expect, but you'll get used to it. Like cows, do you?'

Charlie nodded.

'Good – got a lot of cows. Come on – time for supper, lad – best be off.' The man was out of the hall almost before Charlie had time to move.

The farmhouse was situated down a long dirt track a mile away from the village hall. It had rough-cast walls and a roof of mossy stone tiles. Next to it stood the cowshed, Charlie could smell it as they drove up in the tractor. Below the cowshed was an orchard full of apple trees and beyond that, fields, slanting down to a small stream.

A small woman appeared at the door of the farmhouse.

'Mrs Ackroyd, Charlie – Here's the boy, Alice.'

Charlie nodded at her.

In front of him was a small, bony woman wearing a faded grey dress, her thin, greying hair scrapped back in a tight bun. Her eyes, which slanted downwards at the outer corners, matched the colour of her dress exactly. A grey ghost, Charlie thought before she spoke and broke the illusion.

'Bit small, isn't he?' The farmer's wife looked Charlie up and down carefully as if she was judging his weight. 'Best come in,' she snapped, before turning back into a dark room.

Charlie couldn't see inside for some moments after the glare of the July sun. The first thing that took shape was a large black fire-place, then a mantelpiece with two black china cats with glowing green eyes sitting at each end of it. On the floor of the kitchen was a faded rag-rug lying on top of flagstones. It was a cold room, even in the summer heat. The woman merged into the background as she sat in a rocking chair and started knitting.

'Wash in the sink over there.' She nodded in the direction of a stone sink with a hand pump at the side of it.

Charlie put down his brown leather case that Mary had bought him before he left. The woman stared at it.

'Well, go on then.'

Charlie felt his face flushing. He didn't know what to do.

'What's the matter with you, boy?'

The farmer came in and saw Charlie's confusion.

'Perhaps the lad's not seen one of these before, Alice.' He walked over to the pump and pressed the handle up and down rapidly. Charlie watched the water splash into the big sink. 'Soon get used to it.'

'He'll have to – don't want no fancy ways here. You worked on a farm afore?'

'No,' said Charlie, washing his hands.

'He's a doctor's son, Alice.'

'What!' She shot out of the rocking chair, throwing down the knitting. 'A doctor's son? What use is that to us?' The woman spat the words out before turning to Charlie. 'Hard work's what counts here, boy, and don't you forget it. Up at five a.m. every morning. Bath on Fridays – copper's on the hook behind the door. Empty your chamber pot in the morning and spread it over the garden. Nothing's wasted in this house. Can't afford waste. Not like some.' Her small grey eyes pierced Charlie as she looked at him.

'Give him time to settle in, Alice. He's only just come.' Bert walked over to Charlie and gave him a stiff grey towel to dry his hands. 'You can have a lie-in tomorrow, lad, then I'll learn you. Need another pair of strong hands on the farm … Supper ready, Alice?'

The woman sniffed before banging six white plates down on a large bare wooden table.

'Call Daniel and Ma and Pa.'

Bert Ackroyd went out of the kitchen as the woman put a large cottage loaf and a wedge of cheese on the table. Charlie's stomach was as tight as a drum-skin; he hadn't even been able to eat the sandwiches Mary had given him.

The door suddenly opened and Charlie saw a wiry boy with strong calloused hands and a pimply complexion standing on the threshold. He had the same slanting grey eyes as the woman, and although he wasn't much taller than Charlie, there was the down of a moustache on his upper lip.

'Is this the vaccie, Ma?' he sneered.

It was hate at first sight.

Rose arrived at a lonely Rectory at eight o'clock. It was hidden by a hostile line of fir trees in the village of Benington half a mile away from Charlie. It looked as if it had been built hundreds of years ago for dead people, Rose thought. Its mullioned windows reflected no life.

The two old unmarried sisters, who had taken her there, disappeared immediately they entered the echoing, gloomy hall. Only two weeks ago they'd been told that they must take a child into their home. They had been horrified. Their time was spent reading or writing or listening to their brother's sermons. They wanted no child to disturb the tranquillity of their days.

An old servant, Mabel, took Rose into an ancient kitchen which was built in the time of James I. It housed an enormous fireplace with black fire-irons, a long scrubbed farmhouse table and hundreds of dull copper and pewter pans lining the walls. Rose could feel the damp in the room seep through her thin dress. Mabel was a woman of few words which was why the sisters employed her. She pointed Rose to a hard chair and brought her a glass of milk which she sipped slowly. After three mouthfuls the old servant motioned for her to get up. They entered a small dark room at the back of the house. In one corner Rose saw a narrow, shadowy staircase. Mabel slowly creaked her way up the uneven, winding stairs until they reached a small attic bedroom. She stopped to catch her breath before she spoke.

'This be your room, Miss. Good night.'

The old woman closed the door behind her and Rose heard her creaking down the stairs again. She couldn't stop trembling as she sat on the side of a tiny single bed; there was a room full of butterflies in her stomach. At the side of her bed, on a small washstand was an olive green jug and basin, stencilled with a trellis of pale green ivy.

She got up to wash her hands and face and opened the window. The over-sweet smell of honeysuckle and roses climbed up the trellis-work towards her. And there, in the distance, through her wet eyelashes, she saw a single star, shimmering.

Screams penetrated her sleep. She sat up shaking. Footsteps creaked up the stairs towards her. The door lurched open. A light flashed in her eyes.

'What's the matter, Miss? Why you screaming?'

Rose poked her head over the eiderdown to see the exhausted, wrinkled features of Mabel, the old servant, staring at her in alarm.

'Me, screaming?'

'Yes, Miss – you've gone and woken the whole household. The Vicar and Miss Margaret and Miss Elizabeth – they be most upset.'

A huge black silence lay across the farm as Charlie slept. He was walking uphill on the thorny path, only this time there was no clearing at the top of the hill, just a small house with a thin tendril of smoke coming from the chimney. He knew that the person he was looking for was hiding there. He started to walk towards it, his heart pounding. He stood outside the door and looked up at countless black diamond windows. A shadow moved across an upstairs pane. He opened the front door. Sounds entered his dream. He couldn't understand them.

First a thud that was barely audible, then another, then another, accompanied by a soft rustle. A latch clicked, and clicked again. Then a muffled plod of rubber boots across a yard and the squeak of a door. Then a soft rustling and thumping again. Half awake now, Charlie heard the plod of rubber boots return. A confused pattern of feet and the thwack of a stick. He crawled out of bed and opened the limp curtains; dawn was just breaking over the horizon.

'Whoa!'

Below him in the shadowy farmyard were Bert Ackroyd and his son Daniel, the boy he'd met last night, herding cows out of the yard.

'Whoa there, Blossom!' Bert shouted at a large black and white cow that was jostling another into a fence.

'Houwch! Houwch C'mon you ol' heifers! Houwch!'

'C'mon! Houwch! Houwch!' the boy echoed. 'C'mon you heifers.'

Charlie continued to watch them herd the cows into the field until he was left again with silence. He climbed back into bed and closed his eyes on the coming day.

A lone swallow started to trill. A few grace notes at first, followed by a long interval, until it was joined by a chorus vibrating the morning air. Beyond the emerging hedges and laden orchards, blackbirds and skylarks harmonised to celebrate the dawn. But something was missing. Charlie opened his eyes. Of course, the sound of seagulls and the sea.

Chapter 23

'Your courage; your cheerfulness; your resolution will bring us victory.'

WW II
Ministry of Information Poster

Hilda thought she wouldn't go into the WVS Centre that morning. She didn't have the energy she had when Rose was with her. Every day was a battle that had to be fought. Why had she sent her away? Why had she listened to the authorities? Three children and not one of them living with her. She lay in bed. 7 a.m. and it was hot already. She switched on the wireless. Bill was listening to the other set downstairs. They couldn't afford one, she'd told him, let alone two. Of course, he hadn't listened. *'The news on 26th July 1940 read by Alvar Lidell. Four hundred are feared dead after a German torpedo attack yesterday on a French ship carrying French sailors to Britain.'*

More disasters, she thought, dragging her legs over the bed to switch the wireless off. She must get up. She could hear Mrs Humphries in the garden prattling to her dog, Spot: a black and white terrier. Bill swore he'd put down some poison in the garden if the dog yapped any more. Every time he opened their back door, the dog had convulsions, threatening to tear down the garden fence in an effort to reach his throat.

She sat at the edge of the bed, unable to move until she heard a sound in the sky she couldn't recognise. It wasn't one of theirs. She called down to Bill.

'What is it, Bill?'

'How the hell should I know?'

The next moment, they heard the thud of high explosives in the distance.

Hilda ran down the stairs, the sweat pouring off her.

'Oh my God – it's the start of the invasion, isn't it?'

Bill looked ashen as he rushed out of the front door.

'I'm going to find out. Don't you move from the house, Hilda, 'til I come back.'

She sat on the stairs, her large body shaking with shock.

Half an hour later Hilda was still sitting on the stairs when Bill walked in to tell her about a raider who had swept across the town and unloaded eleven high explosives.

'Where?'

'Some on the cricket ground and others on the West Hill. Need a cup of tea.'

She rushed into the kitchen to make him one.

'Anyone hurt?'

Bill walked in and sat down; he looked exhausted. 'A teacher – just gone to stay with her parents in Priory Road. House demolished. Some others injured. We got to face facts, Hilda – we're in the front line on this coast. It's going to get worse.'

And of course, it did.

The German bombers found Hastings and St Leonards an ideal area to practise their 'tip and run' techniques. Any bombs they had not used over mainland Britain were 'tipped' on the coast before the pilots flew back to Germany. And unfortunately, these lone raiders were unchallenged by any ack-ack fire; the government didn't consider the towns of sufficient military importance at this time to warrant the setting up of AA defences.

Soon notices appeared in the town.

Last year all who could be spared from this town were asked to leave, not only for their own safety, but so as to ease the work of the Armed Forces in repelling an invasion. The danger of invasion has increased and the Government requests all who can be spared and have somewhere to go, to go. If you are in need of help you can have your railway fare paid and a billeting allowance paid to any relative or friend with whom you stay. Take your National Registration card; Identity Card; Ration Book; Gas Mask.

Essential workers will stay.

One morning in August, while Hilda was walking along the sea front, the Cuckoo air raid siren sounded. An air-raid warden came wobbling towards her on his bike, a cardboard sign around his neck saying *Take Cover*. He gesticulated wildly at her, but she carried on walking towards the shops. She was determined to get some fish from the Old Town before it was all sold out.

But this time, before the usual tip and run raiders could fly over the town, they were intercepted by three Spitfire pilots. Hilda felt her heart pounding as she looked out over the sea. In the middle distance, German fighters and bombers were engaged in intense dogfights with the Spitfire pilots. Her shopping bag was dropped on the ground, forgotten, as she watched the Spitfires weaving a pattern of vapour trails in the sky. Soon a small crowd of people were shouting out encouragement to the Spitfire pilots.

'Up and at them, lads!'

'Blast 'em out of the sky!'

'That's the way!' screamed an elderly Home Guard standing next to Hilda as one of the Spitfire's tracers hit a bomber. It plunged into the sea, a lone survivor baling out: his white parachute billowing in the wind.

Everyone held their breath as the Spitfires dived steeply, almost into the sea, pulling out of their dives, seemingly, just before they touched the water, and climbing high through the bombers who suddenly disappeared into the distance.

Hilda threw her arms around the alarmed Home Guard and hugged him. Suddenly, the Spitfires were over their heads. They could see the pilots' young faces as they waggled their wings before flying off towards Biggin Hill. Hilda found her face wet with tears.

That summer, the number of people in the town decreased from 65,000 to just 15,000. But there were those who refused to leave. Hilda was one of them. She was waiting for her children to come home.

'It's bloody daft you staying, Hilda,' Bill told her one day. 'Remember what one of the notices said – the Government might have to evacuate all of us at short notice – it'll be chaos then – we'll be travelling in hot, crowded trains and we won't be able to choose where we go to.'

'Well, why don't you leave? – you're not an essential worker.'

'I'm not leaving my shop to the bloody Jerries to loot and that's final.'

'And I'm not leaving my home for them to trample over and that's final too. Nobody's going to force me out of my home and if Hitler comes to my door I'll shoot the bugger dead.'

Bill looked at her and gave a hoot of laughter.

'My God, Hilda – you're a woman to be reckoned with. Make us a cup of tea, love.'

Hilda bustled round her kitchen and then stopped suddenly. She realised it had taken a war and thirty years before Bill had given her the first compliment of their married life. She gasped.

'Make it yourself. I'm off to see Mary.' Then she took her pinafore off carefully and walked out of the house, leaving Bill sitting in shock at the kitchen table.

Hilda couldn't believe it. It had been so easy. Make it yourself. She'd never said that in thirty years of married life. Why not? She tried to work it out as she walked towards Pevensey Road. She suddenly clamped her hand over her mouth as she thought of the words of a new song she'd heard on the wireless. *"She's a pearl of a wife, no man could have better, so I kiss her good morning and then I forget her."* She'd allowed herself to be a doormat.

An elderly couple trudged slowly towards her and Hilda suddenly raised her fist and shouted.

'Well, I'm not a doormat any more!'

The elderly couple stumbled across the road in alarm.

'Oh dear, oh dear.' The old man wheezed, clutching his heart. 'As if the Jerries are not enough to cope with.'

Hilda saw two small children, a boy and a girl playing in a garden as she walked towards Mary's house. Their high voices carried on the wind.

'No, I'm the doctor – you're the nurse,' the boy said, bossily.

'You be the doctor if you want to!' Hilda shouted out to the little girl whose hair was the colour of lemon grass. The children looked at her, startled. She remembered the games she'd played as a child with her sister and the boys from the local school in the lanes of Catsfield. They were always Red Cross nurses looking after the boys, who were British soldiers in the Boer War.

At least someone has had the sense not to send their children away, Hilda thought, catching her breath, as she walked past them.

Mary and Hilda sat drinking iced lemonade in Mary's beautiful garden and watched vast towers of cumulus rise over the town. The air was heavy with an impending summer storm.

'Look, Hilda.'

Hilda couldn't believe her eyes. The garden was suddenly alive with ants. Triggered by atmospheric pressure they had come up out of their dark subterranean tunnels into hot bright sunlight. They poured out of cracks in the cement path, through holes in the crazy paving; they crawled over Mary's flowerbeds and up her plant stems, some with frail gossamer wings, others wingless.

They watched the ants moving in columns until suddenly, from the tops of plants and tips of grass-stems, the winged ants took off, flying and rising on the thunder thermals to find each other high in the sky; only the fittest males and females mating. They returned to earth a few minutes later, the fertilized queens seeking a soil-crack or hole in which to start their nest. Biting off their wings, for their brief flight of freedom was over, one by one, they returned to the earth.

Then Hilda started crying, quietly, as she watched the ants disappear.

'What's the matter, Hilda?'

She couldn't tell Mary about her marriage. About the horror of lying in bed, night after endless night, next to a man she didn't love.

'Oh – just missing my family that's all. Wishing things were like they were before the war.'

'Well, we can't have that time back, can we?'

The women looked at each other.

'But we could go and see Rose and Charlie, Hilda … I've really missed him. There's no one telling me where to put all our waste any more … no-one asking us questions all the time. He used to drive me mad and now I find myself answering questions in my head I know Charlie would ask me if he was here. Isn't that absurd?'

'No – Rose used to argue all the time … I miss that too.'

'Well, let's go and see them, Hilda.'

Hilda's face flushed. 'I can't, Mary … I'm busy at the centre.'

'You can take one day off to see your daughter, surely?'

Large globules of rain fell into the women's faces as the storm broke over them. Hilda was covered with a sheen of sweat.

'I must be going. Got to get Bill's supper ready.'

Mary raised her eyebrows at Hilda.

'You don't understand … it isn't just …'

She got up to leave. Just as they reached the front door, she turned and said quietly, 'I can't afford the journey, Mary.'

Mary's face flamed with embarrassment.

Later that day John and Mary were sitting in their garden after she'd told him what had happened.

'Can you imagine it? And I'm supposed to be running a Samaritan Centre to help people.'

'Don't be so hard on yourself, my dear,' John said smiling at her. 'I've been guilty of the same mistake.'

'But that doesn't excuse it, does it?'

'No, of course it doesn't.'

They lay back on the green garden chairs, holding hands and enjoying the pleasure they had in each other's company. Mary glanced across at her husband's relaxed features; she had always loved his profile; the strong jaw line belying the sensitive mouth. People always seemed to notice the strength, never the sensitivity. She looked up into the evening sky, washed clean by the storm and wondered if Rob was up there, somewhere. He had always known when she was feeling vulnerable, even as a child.

'Do you know my job's easier since the bombs have started dropping?' John's voice startled her.

'Is it?' She looked at him in surprise. 'How?'

'People don't come to me constantly complaining of nervous disorders any more. Everyone seems to have found a purpose all of a sudden.'

'All those who've stayed, you mean.'

'Yes, I suppose you're right – I haven't got so many patients, have I?' John smiled with his eyes closed.

'What do you think Charlie is doing at this precise moment?' Mary asked

'God knows – taking over the Ackroyd's farm by the sound of his letters. You miss him, don't you?'

'Remember the night you tried to bath him?'

John chuckled.

'You don't think he hates us, do you, John, for sending him away?'

He opened his eyes and looked at Mary's troubled face.

'No, I don't think he hates us – I think he's angry with us.'

'I want to go to see him, but I can't go without Rose's mother.'

John looked across the garden at Charlie's vegetable plot. Mary had been trying to make the vegetables grow as Charlie did, but most of the beans and peas had already shrivelled.

'What about this as an idea, Mary? You know the conference I'm going to at Guy's in a couple of weeks? Why don't you and Mrs Brazier come up with me and travel from there to Hertfordshire. It's not much further, is it? What do you think?'

'I think you're brilliant, darling.'

Chapter 24

'O aching time. O moments big as years.'

John Keats
Hyperion 1, 1818

After the first morning, Bert Ackroyd took Charlie out every day to show him the workings of the farm. In a month he had learned how to herd the cows into the field; how to fill the hay troughs for their feeds; how to pick the best fruit in the orchard and how to avoid Daniel Ackroyd after milking. But he couldn't get the hang of milking. He dreaded getting up at dawn to repeat his previous failures. Daniel Ackroyd loved it. He positioned himself on a three-legged stool opposite Charlie every morning so that he could sneer at his attempts at milking.

'Put your cheek against the cow,' Bert Ackroyd had told Charlie, 'and pull hard on the teats, but not too hard, mind – don't want her going skittish on us.'

What he hadn't told Charlie was how hard milking was on the fingers; after ten minutes the pain was excruciating. He watched the effortless rhythm of the others. The whole family was involved in milking. Every morning Bert, Alice and Daniel, Grandma and Grandfer milked the herd silently. Grandma was smaller than Charlie, so bent she looked as if she had curvature of the spine. She reminded Charlie of a shrivelled turkey: the skin of her neck like a piece of chamois leather that had been wrung out and left to dry in desiccated folds. But it was the old man, Grandfer, that Charlie was frightened of. His nose looked like a disease, enormous and red and swollen in lumps. He shouted because he was deaf and talked to himself all the time. And yet, old as Grandma and Grandfer were, they could both milk a cow dry almost before Charlie had time to sit down on his stool.

He couldn't seem to get the milk into the bucket; it either squirted over him or over the green-stained cowshed floor. He saw Daniel sniggering from the other side of the cowshed. He called over to Charlie. 'Too 'ard for a townie, is it?' Then he shouted to his father 'Pa – vaccie here still can't do it proper!'

Charlie struggled to control the hard ball of anger in his chest as he looked at the boy's sneering face.

Bert Ackroyd walked over and peered into Charlie's empty bucket.

'You'll never make a cowman, young 'un.'

'I don't want to be a bloody cowman – I want to be a fighter pilot!' Charlie kicked the bucket and crashed out of the cowshed.

The old folk shook their heads. 'No good 'll come o' that temper o' his. Mark m'words,' said Grandma through stitched lips.

The next day Charlie had to help Grandma and Grandfer in the orchard, collecting the fruit. His job was to climb the wide-bottomed ladders which rested against the old trees and collect the fruit from the top branches. He'd been doing it for hours. He climbed down the last tree and watched the old woman bend double to grasp ripe windfalls from under another tree and put them carefully in the wooden trug she carried in the crook of her elbow. Her liver-spotted hands moved with a regular lever-like action, back and forth through the windfalls. She looked as if she had grown in the orchard, alongside the trees, Charlie thought. All of them had names, she had told him. *Fairy. Damson. Bluebell.* Strange names for trees, but then, they were a strange family.

'Fairy's not fruitin' well this year,' she called out to him. 'Only good for maggots, but Bluebell'll bring in a bob or two.'

'How old is Bluebell?' Charlie asked, sitting down at the base of the old tree.

'Old as I. Older, mebbe.'

Her claw-like fingers swept through the long branches, fingering for half-hidden fruit. She pinched them slightly, before levering them into the trug by her elbow. 'Umm – some of 'em windfalls only good for cider.' She looked up at Charlie suddenly. 'Afore the war, me and Grandfer lived in Sussex, you see.' She nodded slowly, as if that explained something.

Which war did she mean? thought Charlie. They both looked old enough to have lived through hundreds; especially the old man with that nose of his. Grandfer walked right past Charlie every day talking to the vegetables, his huge hands dangling down his giant's body. He looked like a vegetable himself, Charlie thought. A vegetable pulling up other vegetables with enormous root-like fingers.

At lunch-time, Charlie went back to the farmhouse to lie down. He'd worked for six exhausting hours. He took off his boots at the door as Mrs Ackroyd hated dirt being carried into the house. A cough came from one of the bedrooms. He frowned. Everyone was working outside. He crept up the stairs and saw that the door of his small bedroom was open. Daniel Ackroyd was sitting on his bed, sniggering, as he read Charlie's latest letter from Rob, hidden under his mattress. Charlie's vision clouded as a sudden surge of blood pounded through his brain. He heard the sound of roaring in the distance and suddenly Daniel's thin neck was under his fingers and he was squeezing tight. He watched the boy's face turn purple and his body fighting to be free of the fingers. Suddenly, Charlie released him. The boy collapsed onto the floor, taking in great sobbing gulps of air as Charlie snatched Rob's letter out of his hand and stuffed it into his pocket.

'Ma! Pa!' Daniel screamed, running down the stairs. 'Vaccie's tried to kill me!'

Charlie didn't wait to find out what happened. He decided to run away. He knew if he didn't, he really would kill Daniel, and he didn't want to be put into prison. He started to walk across the fields, trampling through clouds of cowslips. He forgot his clothes and suitcase left at the farm; he wanted to distance himself from the anger he felt. He walked through the weight of the orchard, laden with late summer fruit, and focused on Grandma's bent body in the distance; she was still plucking fruit from the trees. The farm spread out around him in the glowing sun – the upper fields where he'd helped stack the haystacks; the beech trees where he'd seen a badger; the overgrown pond where he'd found adders and fritillary butterflies. Suddenly, he heard screaming from the farmhouse and set his face towards the Rectory and Rose.

Rose was in church. She spent most of her time in church now, either helping Miss Margaret and Miss Elizabeth decorate it with flowers or brushing the embroidered hassocks on the pews. The ladies had embroidered them all with white crosses as a sign of devotion to God and their brother Algie.

Rose didn't like churches – they reminded her of death: damp and cold. There was no joy here. There was no joy at the Rectory. She wondered, as she listened to the vicar's endless sermons over the weeks, why God wanted religion to be so solemn, so unfriendly, so boring. But she learned to play her part well. The sisters didn't suspect her of being a heretic because she could sing hymns beautifully. She had sung hymns in school, but only half-heartedly because nobody seemed to care about them. But Miss Margaret and Miss Elizabeth and the vicar did. They told her that Jesus was listening to every note she sang, watching every movement she made, knew every thought she was thinking. It was terrifying. How could she control her thoughts? So one night, she decided to sing her way to heaven with hymns. She thought she must be halfway to heaven by now as she'd been in the church choir for weeks.

She sang the last note of *'Fight the Good Fight'* and looked up at the stone knight on top of a corbel, his body pierced with a sword. Under the north wall of the chancel, she could see two enormous larger-than-life effigies: another knight, this time, cross-legged, next to a lady wearing a wimple. Who was the lady with the wimple? Why was the knight on the corbel trying to kill himself? And why was the other knight sitting cross-legged? She asked the sisters. But they'd never answered, just whispered to each other as they arranged more honeysuckle and roses around the church. Rose couldn't understand why religion was shrouded in so much mystery.

The vicar coughed to announce the beginning of another sermon and the congregation drooped as his monochrome tones droned over their heads. He told them about Amraphel, King of Shinar, Ariioch, King of Ellasar, Chedoraomer, King of Elam and Shinab, King of Admah. Rose wondered why everyone in the Bible had such unpronounceable names. She yawned discreetly, almost without moving her mouth. Last Sunday, the vicar had told the congregation, after an enormously lengthy preamble, that they must love their neighbours as themselves. She wondered how anyone could love Hitler or Mrs Humphries – except perhaps Spot, her dog, and he was half-blind and retarded. She couldn't understand why one week God was all for 'an eye for an eye' and the next for 'turning the other cheek'. Rose suspected God suffered from inconsistency. And how could you follow the teachings of someone who was always changing his mind?

She could always tell when the vicar had finished talking because everyone shuffled and woke up. She had taught herself to drift up into the medieval lancet stained-glass windows with her eyes open. No one knew she wasn't in the choir stalls. She liked to stand in front of a benign Jesus in a blue robe staring down at her with one hand lifted to make the sign of the cross. This cross, the sisters had told her, would save her. They hadn't told her from what. The words underneath read: *'Jesus Prays for All Sinners.'* He really must be exhausted Rose thought, as she looked across at all the people in the church she'd heard being malicious about each other in the village shop.

'Hymn No. 298.'

Rose turned the pages of her red buckram hymn book and her rich young soprano voice floated angelically around the choir stalls.

'Lead, kindly Light, amid the encircling gloom
Lead thou me on;
The night is dark, and I am far from home;
Lead thou me on.'

The words suddenly choked in her throat and large tears dripped down onto her virginal white dress.

Chapter 25

'Chaos often breeds life,
when order breeds habit.'

Henry Brooks Adams
Education of Henry Adams, 1907

John, Mary and Hilda arrived in London on a gorgeous afternoon in September. John went to Guy's Hospital for his conference; Mary and Hilda to Lyons Corner House in Piccadilly for lunch before travelling up to Hertfordshire.

Hilda looked around at the gigantic room with its ornate gold and green counter, and its hundreds of waitresses balancing large plates of food, pots of tea, sugar and milk, all on one tray. Thank God I don't have to serve people any more, she thought. Then suddenly her face flushed; she realised that that was exactly what she'd been doing for years married to Bill – serving him.

'I really enjoyed that,' said Mary putting down her knife and fork after finishing off a large plate of roast beef and Yorkshire pudding.

Hilda sniffed. 'Umm – don't think the Yorkshire pudding was as good as mine to be honest, Mary.'

'Well it was ten times better than mine, Hilda, I can tell you.'

The women laughed. Mary had seldom relaxed with anyone outside her family before. It was a good feeling.

'Hilda – I've been thinking. Why don't we go up to Hertfordshire tomorrow and stay overnight in London? Didn't you say your sister lived here?'

Hilda looked startled. 'Oh I couldn't do that, Mary.'

'Why not? Isn't your sister on the telephone?'

'Yes ... it's not ... it's ... Bill. He wouldn't like me staying up here alone.'

'You won't be alone. You'll be with me.'

'And how would I let him know? – we're not on the telephone.'

Mary thought quickly. 'Doesn't Mrs Bates live near you? She's got a telephone. Give her a ring and ask her to tell your husband you'll be coming back tomorrow. The journey's far too long to do in one day, anyway. Oh, come on, Hilda – when did you last enjoy yourself? I can't remember the last time I did. Do you like the theatre? – I haven't been to the theatre for years. How would you like to go and see a Noel Coward comedy?'

Hilda rearranged her knife and fork. Why did Mary always forget how different their backgrounds were?

Mary looked at Hilda's withdrawn face.

'Look, it's my treat. I hate going to the theatre by myself and John always goes to sleep when I drag him there. Please. Let's just enjoy ourselves and forget the war for a little while. The children don't even know we're coming, do they? Come on, Hilda – let's live a little.'

Hilda looked at Mary and suddenly smiled. She was right – but Hilda didn't want to live a little, she wanted to live a lot.

'I'd love to go to the theatre,' she said.

Mary and Hilda enjoyed every minute of Noel Coward's *Blithe Spirit*. They came out of the Piccadilly Theatre to an ominous sky, but even the weather couldn't dampen their pleasure.

'Oh Mary, when that woman, Madame Arcati, had a séance and conjured up her host's dead wife, I thought I'd die laughing.'

'I told you we'd enjoy ourselves. Wasn't Fay Compton good as the second wife?'

But Mary didn't hear Hilda's answer because the stomach-churning sounds of an air-raid siren flooded the twilight air and suddenly the street was full of running people. The women looked up, and out of nowhere, a black rash of enemy aircraft came flying towards them. They stood, unable to move, as the heavy drone of a giant V of German bombers flew overhead, surrounded by the sun-glint of fighters weaving in and out of them. They heard the awesome scream of bombs descending and suddenly they were sprawling headlong across the pavement.

Hilda held her arms over her head and listened to what sounded like a giant sheet tearing as an HE bomb fell on the other end of the Strand. Then the rattle of incendiaries on roofs and the pierce of shrapnel on the pavements.

Then silence.

She gingerly lifted her head and saw Mary staring at her with an astonished look on her face; she was covered with a cloud of grey dust and her smart navy suit was in shreds. Hilda sat up and started laughing. Mary got up carefully, coughing as she brushed the dust off her skirt.

'Mary – I'm still alive! … You're still alive!' Hilda was shouting with laughter. And suddenly, Mary was laughing too, looking down in wonder at her intact body.

'I can't believe it, Hilda – not a scratch on me – only dust. What about you?'

Hilda checked her body and found a splinter of glass in her arm and a large tear in her dress. 'A small cut – that's all.' The thin ribbon of blood trickling down Hilda's arm was a miracle.

Across the road, a man started his car up and weaved through the debris on the Strand. He gave them a thumbs-up sign as he drove past them.

'You know where we're going, Hilda?'

Hilda shook her head; she couldn't seem to stop laughing.

'We're going for a drink in the Savoy?'

'What – like this?' Hilda shouted, crossing over the littered street to collect her handbag which had somehow sailed through the air to land in a sea of broken glass.

'Yes, just like this,' shouted Mary laughing, her curly brown hair still covered in a grey layer of dust.

The women crunched up the cracked pavement towards the Savoy unable to stop talking and laughing. Everything was wonderful: the Strand, frosted with millions of fragments of broken glass; the acrid cocktail of dust and smoke-charred timbers; the clang of fire-engines arriving to put out the incendiaries. But best of all was an old newspaper-seller, calmly selling papers to people who emerged from the shelters into the debris of shrapnel.

'Biggest raid ever!' the old man shouted. 'England 115! Germany nil! Still batting!'

Mary gave him 6d for a 1d newspaper. Other people were doing the same. His face glowed.

'Ta, luv,' he said to Mary. 'Few more raids like that and I can retire to Streatham.'

The doorman at the Savoy took in the sight of Mary and Hilda's clothes without a blink of an eye, as if he'd spent a lifetime opening doors to dusty women with blood running down their arms and large holes in their clothes. He bowed to them both.

'Good evening, Madam … Madam.'

'Good evening,' they chorused as if they always came out in shredded, dust-covered clothes to drink in the West End. For once, Hilda wasn't overawed by the ornate crimson velvet furnishings in the foyer. She followed Mary to the powder room where they laughed at the state of their clothes and washed the dust off their faces.

'What would you like to drink, Hilda?' Mary said, once they arrived at the famous River Room: a restaurant and cabaret bar. The place was crowded with people who were obviously waiting for a cabaret artist to arrive.

'Port and lemon, please, Mary,' said Hilda, feeling incredibly wicked as she sat down on one of the bar stools.

'And a whisky and soda for me,' said Mary to the bar man. She turned to Hilda. 'I wonder who they're waiting for.'

The atmosphere in the room was electric; everyone wanted to celebrate the fact that they were still alive after the raid.

They could see a large party of people drinking champagne on a distant table. Mary leaned over to Hilda.

'You know who that large man is – the one with the enormous cigar in his mouth?'

Hilda shook her head. She had never ever been in such a wonderful place in her life. She was floating on air.

'It's Sir Henry 'Chips' Channon, the millionaire, and sitting next to him is our new President of the Board of Trade.'

Suddenly everyone started clapping as a middle-aged man, with immaculate Brylcreamed hair and a well-tailored dinner-suit stood in the doorway, accepting the accolades. 'Chips' stood up to call to him.

'Noel, old boy – we're over here.'

Hilda gasped. She had seen Noel Coward's photograph outside the Piccadilly Theatre. 'Mary – it's him!'

They watched him wave a nonchalant arm in the direction of Chips' table as he shook the many hands that were thrust into his path.

'A song, Mr Coward, if you please,' shouted a man from a corner of the restaurant.

The refrain was echoed around the room.

Noel Coward smiled as he looked at everyone and sauntered over to the microphone. 'Ladies and Gentlemen – as you insist on my entertaining you and as long you all realise I relish criticism – just so long as it's unqualified praise.' Everyone laughed as he sat down at the piano. 'Here's a song I've just written called *"Don't Let's Be Beastly to the Germans"*.'

Mary watched the enjoyment on people's faces fade as Noel Coward launched into a languid song about 'turning the other cheek' to the Hun. The audience had been prepared for comedy, not satire; the song was followed by a stunned silence.

'Oh dear, not the best choice after a raid, was it?' Mary said, on her second large whisky and soda. She was leaning at a very odd angle, Hilda noticed.

A balding man with a very red face got up and shouted. 'That's your idea of humour, is it? You unpatriotic bastard!'

Noel Coward stood up from the piano, looked at the oysters on the man's plate and breathed into the microphone. 'Ladies and Gentlemen – you know what they say about oysters? – oysters and poverty share the same bed.'

There were a few guffaws around the room as he walked nonchalantly over to Chips Channon's table and sat down next to his millionaire friend.

Hilda watched herself walking over to their table from some distance away. She could vaguely hear Mary calling her back.

They all looked up in surprise as Hilda's large shape loomed over the table.

'I went to see *Blithe Spirit* this afternoon,' she said to Noel Coward. 'Thoroughly enjoyed it.'

'Ah, that's what I like to hear, dear lady,' said Noel, waving a glass of champagne in Hilda's direction. 'Unqualified praise.'

'But you know what they say about men with short bodies? Brains too near their bottoms.'

She walked back towards Mary in a circular direction, smiling to herself.

Chapter 26

'The ruling passion be it what it will
The ruling passion conquers reason still.'

Alexander Pope (1688-1744)
Moral Essays

The hut had been a hive of activity for days. Bridget had been mixing shoe polish with face cream to make a rich foundation. Midge had told them about gravy browning; if mixed with water and rubbed on their legs, they would look as if they'd been on the Riviera. A few of them had stolen a bottle from the cookhouse at night. Jan discovered Norma, the Metal Panda, had been hoarding a large oval cake of Elizabeth Arden geranium perfumed soap in her locker for weeks and had requisitioned it for their baths before the dance. Daisy revealed that she'd been a hairdresser before she joined up, but had decided at seventeen that she wasn't 'cut out' for the job. But on this night of special nights, she'd transform their hair. Tiny Midge had been drawing a black line with an eyebrow pencil up the back of any girls' legs who didn't have seamed stockings. Kate had melted almond oil on the stove in the middle of the hut with lipstick-ends to use as rouge. Armpits had been dusted with bicarbonate of soda to stop perspiration, margarine wrappers had been rubbed into skin to soften it and mascara had been invented from burned cork. They had spent hours preening, plucking and basting to create new faces. Two hours later, they all looked in wonder at the perfumed strangers parading up and down their hut in their best dresses.

'Holy Mary,' said Bridget, 'I don't recognise a face in the hut at all.'

'Where's Tessa?' Maggie said. They all looked around.

Kate realised that she'd been so involved with her preparations for the last few hours she hadn't missed her. Suddenly the door opened and there she stood, looking more stunning than Ingrid Bergman in a shimmering blue dress. Her hair, a glowing peroxide yellow, was flowing over her shoulders in the latest Eugene waves; her fingernails and toenails were painted bright red to match her lipstick and she was wearing silk stockings. They all gasped.

'Where did you get that dress?' said Kate, her mouth an O of astonishment.

'I rang Mummy and she brought it over in the car,' Tessa answered casually, aware of the effect she was having on everyone.

Kate had felt wonderful in the blue dress she had bought with the last of her clothing rations, but Tessa's arrival made her feel inadequate. She looked around the room and saw the glow die on everyone's face. Tessa diminished them all by looking so beautiful.

Jan swore as she pushed past Tessa. 'You toffee-nosed cow.'

'What have I done?' she purred as she walked elegantly out of the hut.

The Mess Hall had been decorated with coloured streamers and balloons; some of the men on the camp had scoured Wolverhampton looking for them and had bought back hundreds. Then they had set up a small stage for the band. The girls gasped as they walked into the Mess; it had been transformed. But then, Kate thought, it is almost our last night together. She looked around at the WAAFs, standing in groups, depending on which hut they shared.

'Penny for them, Kate?' Bridget walked up to her, looking radiant in a dark green dress, her auburn hair tied up with a green ribbon. 'I don't know why you're looking so sad – you look grand.'

'Not as grand as Tessa though,' Kate said, looking across the room. Tessa was already surrounded by a group of officers.

'Now tell me – how could you look as grand as her?' said Bridget, grinning.

'I wonder how many of us will ever meet again after we're posted.'

'Well – you're lumbered with me now, aren't you? Although the Virgin Mary only knows why you'd want to be.'

Kate smiled at her. Over the last few months, she and Bridget had become firm friends and had asked to be posted together. Bridget always brushed her shadows away.

'Mind you,' Bridget said, breaking through Kate's thoughts, 'there's others I could do without now.'

She turned to stare at Norma who was sitting rigidly on a hard chair, talking to another WAAF. They were looking at Tessa, obviously disapproving of her success with men.

There was a large number of servicemen at the other end of the room by the bar, laughing as they looked across at the girls.

'I hate that, don't you, when they laugh?' said Bridget. 'You never know if they're talking about you.' She looked around for the Canadians. 'They haven't arrived, then?'

'Who?' asked Kate.

'Dear God, Kate – you're so transparent. You know exactly who I mean. Why did you spend so many hours rubbing things into your face?'

Kate was just about to state her complete indifference to Canadians when people started clapping. The four piece band had arrived and soon the room was full of the strains of the song *'Jealousy'*.

'A bit early in the evening to be playing that, wouldn't you say?' Bridget said, just as the door opened and forty-five Canadians walked in. The WAAFs' postures changed imperceptibly, but none of them, except Maggie, looked in their direction. The men walked straight over to the bar. Bridget nudged Kate.

'He's looking at you, Kate.'

Kate glanced across the room; there was Mike standing with a bunch of flowers smiling at her. His friends wolf-whistled.

An hour later, the temperature in the room had heated up as couple after couple danced tangos and quick-steps and sambas. Then suddenly, the band started playing '*The Beer Barrel Polka'* and soon the room was full of wild young people dancing the polka in a riot of pleasure. Kate could feel her blood racing as the band reached the last bar and she and Mike came to a breathless halt in the middle of the crowded dance floor. Everyone was laughing and clapping, except Norma who still sat watching the proceedings from the same chair with the same disapproving look.

People fought their way towards the bar to get a drink to cool down. Kate got separated from Mike in the throng of sweating bodies. She moved away from the bar and sat down in a corner. In another crowded corner, she could see Bridget standing next to the Canadian who'd undressed her with his eyes in the truck. But now he was looking at her with love-lorn eyes, while Bridget was looking around at all the other men in the room. She saw Kate and waved. Kate waved back, smiling. She looked around at all the smiling faces and felt suddenly isolated from the mass of happy people. Soon she would be leaving for her new posting in Cranfield. Her life seemed to be a series of goodbyes.

The band struck up '*Run Rabbit Run Rabbit, Run, Run, Run*' and soon a long line of bodies, their arms criss-crossed behind their backs, swept past Kate, kicking and shouting in a tribal dance. Bridget was laughing in the middle of them. She had such a capacity for enjoyment, Kate thought. Mike walked over with her glass of cider.

'Fancy joining the dance?' he shouted over the noise.

Kate shook her head and shouted back. 'War dances aren't my cup of tea.'

He laughed. 'You English say such funny things.'

Kate smiled at him. 'Can't hear you,' she shouted, drinking deeply from the cool glass of cider.

'Oh, yes you can.' He smiled back at her. 'Want some fresh air?'

She nodded; it was stiflingly hot in the room. They walked past the tribal dancing out into a moonlit night. Mike forgot to close the door behind them and someone slammed it shut.

'Hell – I keep forgetting the black-out,' he said.

'So do I.'

The night air was cool after the steam of the hall. Kate lifted up her face to feel the breeze. 'Oh, that's lovely.'

'So are you, Kate.'

She felt woozy from the cider. She had never tasted anything so strong before.

'Oh, wartime talk.'

He looked hurt. 'No, it's not. You *are* lovely. Why can't you take a compliment?'

'Not used to them, I suppose.'

'I can't believe that.'

He moved towards her and kissed her. She could taste his beer in her mouth. It was pleasant. Mingles well with cider, she thought, giggling.

'Hey, you're not supposed to giggle when a guy kisses you.'

'Aren't you? I always giggle when men kiss me.'

'Are you drunk?'

'I certainly am.'

'Hell, I want you to kiss me because you want to, not because the drink tells you to.'

'Drink isn't telling me anything. Come here.'

She grabbed his jacket and pulled him towards her and tried to kiss him.

'Kate – this isn't you, is it? I've been buying you too much booze.'

The next moment she was dancing around the grass outside the Mess singing *'Who's Sorry Now'*. Then she suddenly stopped and started sobbing.

Mike came and put his arms around her. 'Jesus – you sure are one complicated girl. Come on – I'll take you back to your hut.'

'No, I want to dance, Mike. Let's go back to the Mess. It's only because I'm leaving. I hate endings.'

And Kate pulled him back into the dance just as the band was winding up the night with Cole Porter's *'Night and Day'*. The poignant refrain wafted around the intertwined bodies of service men and women who knew that this was the last time most of them would ever touch each other again. For Kate, held close in Mike's arms, the pain was almost physical.

'Have you any idea how long a night can last spent lying alone?' she whispered in his ear.

He moved back to look at her. 'You know what you're saying, don't you?'

'I've got four days left … that's all.'

Chapter 27

'There is all the difference in the world
between having something
to say and having to say something.'

John Dewey
Education and Experience, 1938

Charlie and Rose were walking across an area overgrown with gorse and blackthorn, dock-leaves and thistles. The sun had dropped behind an escarpment and swirls of coppery clouds were trailing over the rim. Thorns had torn at their socks, their legs were criss-crossed with blood and Rose had been bitten by numerous insects.

'I thought the countryside was supposed to be lovely. I hate it,' Rose said, rubbing all the bites on her hand. She could already see them becoming swollen.

'We've got lots of countryside round us in Hastings. You like that.'

'Yes, but that's nice countryside. Look.' Rose held out her arm with its lumpy bites for Charlie's sympathy.

'I always react badly to bites, my Mum says, but she always puts something on them. She's got a jar with dock leaves soaked in alcohol. It always gets rid of the itching. Go away!' She shouted, swinging her arms at the horseflies that were following them.

'And I'm a fiddler's monkey.'

'What?'

'How can dock-leaves and alcohol get rid of bites?'

'Cos they do. My Mum says!'

'Oh, and your Mum knows everything, does she?'

'More than yours does and anyway you never see yours, do you?'

She saw the pain on Charlie's face.

'Sorry, Charlie. Didn't mean it.'

They came to a tall hawthorn hedge at the edge of the field. It was covered in the yellow and orange colours of toadflax. Charlie's face was brushed by the Chinese dragon's whiskers of its long pointed petals as he climbed through a small gap in the hedge.

'Wait for me, Charlie,' Rose shouted, squeezing through the gap after him, wincing as she scratched her swollen arms on the hedge.

They came out onto a stubble field which had just been harvested. It glowed in the late autumnal sunlight as if waiting to be painted. Rose hurried past sweet-smelling straw, full of red poppies and beautiful yellow and purple fluellen.

'I'm sorry, Charlie. You know my mouth's too big for my face.'

'You said it.' Charlie broke off a branch from an elder tree to whisk the flies away.

'Will you break one for me?'

'No,' he said, walking off across the field.

'Wait for me!' Rose called, fighting with a branch that wouldn't break. 'Charlie help me!'

'Help yourself!'

Rose blinked back the tears in her eyes. 'All right then – I will!' She gave an enormous tug on the branch and it suddenly snapped, throwing her into the stubble. Charlie looked back at her furious face and grinned.

'It's not funny, Charlie Slater!'

'It's the funniest thing I've ever seen, Rose Brazier.'

She jumped up. 'Oh, is it?' she said, stubbornly pulling the enormous branch behind her.

'How's that going to stop horseflies biting you?' he shouted, walking backwards. 'They going to fall in it, are they?' He fell over a sheaf of barley and collapsed onto the field, helpless with laughter.

Rose walked towards him and flopped down. 'I'm tired, Charlie. We've been walking for hours.'

They sat in silence, watching the clouds making pictures in the sky.

Suddenly, they saw the wink of a small eye in the long grass. In the distance was a small field-mouse: its huge light-collecting eyes staring; its radar ears swivelling to detect the faintest sound. Then out of the dusk air, came a barn-owl, drifting along the margin of the field, its blur born of the subtle hues of early evening. It hovered, bright eyes focusing on the mouse, then suddenly plummeted into the grass; legs extended; scimitar claws piercing. A quick death.

'Oh that's so cruel,' Rose shuddered. 'The poor mouse.'

'No, it's not. It's killing because it's hungry. People kill all the time when they don't need to. That's cruel,' Charlie said, getting up. 'C'mon, we've got to get to the wood before it gets dark.'

'A wood? What are we going to a wood for?' Rose asked, following him across the field.

'We're going to hide until the morning.'

Her face went white. 'I don't want to hide in a wood, Charlie. All sorts of things will be in there.'

'What sort?'

Rose looked embarrassed. 'I don't know, do I? I've never slept in a wood before.'

'Well then … or do you want the old girls to find you and take you back to the Rectory?'

Rose shook her head.

'Then c'mon,' he said, walking towards the wood's cloak of camouflage.

A blackbird suddenly emerged from a thick cluster of ivy, interlaced with the tendrils of old man's beard which covered an oak tree. It was joined by a robin, which bobbed and bowed with a persistent tic-tic above the heads of the children as they walked deeper into the wood, crushing fungi under their feet.

'Charlie – it's getting dark.' The trees were becoming grey silhouettes. Rose wanted to go home.

'It's all right – it's safe. There's only us here and the stars.' He looked up. 'Look there's Venus shining at us, Rose.'

'I don't want to look at stars. I'm scared.'

'It's all right, Rosie – I know what to do. We'll make a bivouac when I find the right spot.'

'What's that?'

'A sort of camp where we'll be dry. I've read about them in Rob's books. We've just got to get lots of branches and twigs and sort of weave them together.'

'How do we do that?'

'It's easy,' said Charlie, trying to sound confident.

The children worked for half-an-hour as the light withdrew and darkness descended. Then they crawled into their bivouac and Charlie brought a torch out of his pocket and switched it on. They looked at each other in the glow of the torch-light.

'You didn't say you had a torch.'

'Well, I have.' He looked around their miniature house. 'See, I told you. We're safe here.'

'Are you hungry?' she asked him.

'What if I am? There's nothing to eat.'

'Yes, there is.' Rose suddenly pulled out a loaf of bread and some cheese from the small bag she had been carrying all day. 'There we are.'

Charlie's eyes lit up. 'You didn't say you had some food.'

'Well, I have.' Rose grinned as she passed him some bread.

'Did you nick this from the Rectory? Blimey, you'll never go to heaven now, will you?' He grabbed some cheese from her.

Rose groaned. 'Oh no – I never thought of that. We can't eat it. God will be looking at us.'

'I was joking, Rosie. He can't be watching everyone, can he? Millions of people in the world. He'd have to have millions of eyes, wouldn't he? And where's it say in the Bible that God's got millions of eyes?'

'How do you know about the Bible?'

'A Priest used to come to our house and tell us stories from it when I was a kid. He never said nothing about hundreds of eyes. I reckon God'll be looking at all the other people.'

'What other people?'

'People like Hitler and Mrs Humphries. How can he be bothered about us eating some bread and cheese?'

Rose's stomach rumbled as she thought about it. 'It's not a lot of food, is it?'

'Naw,' Charlie said, chomping his way through half a loaf of bread. 'Bet the vicar's got hundreds of loaves and fishes stashed away at the Rectory.'

'Think so?' said Rose, eating the other half of the loaf. She suddenly looked at Charlie. 'Why did a Priest come to your house?'

Charlie chewed his bread and cheese for some time before answering her. 'Me Mum's a Catholic.'

'What's that?'

'Dunno, except we had a cross on the wall and the Priest came to the house a lot cos we never went to church.'

'My Mum's a Pro … Pros … Protestant.'

'What's that?'

'Dunno, but we never had a Priest coming to our house and we never went to church either.' They listened to a sudden flurry of wind outside the bivouac. 'Charlie?' Rose blinked in the torchlight.

'Yeah?'

'What's your Dad like?'

'What's yours?' he snapped.

'Mine?' Rose was taken aback for a minute. 'He gets cross, sometimes. Don't know why.'

'Yeah, so did mine.'

'Charlie?'

'Miss me brothers,' he said, quickly.

'How many you got?'

'Three. Mickey's five. Alfie's eight and Jimmy's ten.'

'Must be nice having younger brothers. You can tell them what to do. Everyone tells me what to do in my house.' Rose wiped her face and hands on a handkerchief she had in her bag.

Charlie snorted. 'You wouldn't tell our Jimmy what to do. Real hard nut he is. We used to smash all the kids in the street we did.'

'Why?'

Charlie looked at her. 'Before they smashed us, of course, and we had to look out for Mickey and Alf.'

'Sounds awful. Everyone fighting.' She yawned loudly and curled up on a carpet of leaves.

Charlie picked up some twigs and played with them. 'We didn't fight all the time. Sometimes we went to the market and nicked things.'

Rose rolled over to look at him. 'But stealing's wrong, isn't it? My Mum was ever so angry when Mrs Adams came to our house and told her about us stealing in Woolworths.'

'Yeah, I know… but I think it depends on why people do it. Take this bread… we might have starved to death –'

'To death?' Rose said, her eyes enormous in the torchlight.

'Yeah – if you hadn't taken it – and the vicar's got lots more, so that's all right, isn't it?'

'Do you think God thinks like that?'

'Course he does. Look at Jesus – how do you think he did all them miracles if he didn't do a bit of nicking. And he's the son of God, isn't he?'

Rose thought about this. 'D'you mean – like Father, like son?'

'No, I don't!' Charlie shouted.

'Don't bite my head off. You've got an awful temper.'

'So have you.'

'No, I haven't, Charlie Slater!' Rose shouted back at him.

Charlie grinned at her in the torch light and suddenly Rose grinned back.

'Pax?' Charlie said.

'Pax,' she answered. 'Do you want to go home, Charlie?' Rose could feel her eyes closing.

'Yeah. Miss the sea.'

'But your home's in London.'

Charlie switched off the torch and lay down.

'Night,' he said abruptly in the dark.

'Charlie? Don't put the torch off. I'm frightened of the dark.'

'Got to. Battery's running low. Nothing to be scared of here, Rose. There's no people.'

'My Mum'll kill me when she finds out I'm gone,' she said sleepily. She put out her hand and squeezed his. 'Night, Charlie.'

'How can she kill you if you're not there, you silly girl?' But there was no answer and soon Charlie heard the deep rhythm of her sleeping breath. 'Anyway, Rosie, there's worst things to be frightened of than the dark,' he said, whispering into the night.

Chapter 28

'The afternoon of human life must also have a significance of its own
and cannot be merely a pitiful appendage to life's morning.'

Carl Jung
The Stages of Life, 1930

Hilda's head had stopped hurting by the time they reached Hatfield, although how Mary had found the way without any signs was a mystery to her. She was worried about seeing Rose; she was worried about seeing Bill when she got back. He wouldn't be pleased. He'd never had to cook for himself before. How would he manage?

'Bill likes his potatoes cooked for nine minutes and his vegetables for four,' her mother-in-law had told her when she and Bill were first married.

'All his vegetables?' Hilda asked her.

The woman had looked at her contemptuously. 'Of course, all his vegetables.'

They had lived with her for four years before they could afford a place of their own.

'Isn't it wonderful, Hilda?' Mary said, cutting through her thoughts. Hilda looked around at the countryside, heavy with beauty, and realised she was right. She saw the last taste of summer in the wild flowers she'd walked through as a child: Ragwort, purple Knapweed, blue tufts of Selfheal and Herb Robert with its geranium-scented leaves. She smiled, remembering picking Herb Robert with her mother on the banks of streams and watching her crush the seed heads to use as a remedy for all ills – from staunching blood to curing sore throats. But it hadn't saved her.

'Are you all right, Hilda? I should never have encouraged you to drink. I'm sorry, it was stupid of me but –'

'No, it's not your fault, Mary. It was the raid. Anyway, my headache's gone … but I'm not doing it again, mind you. Can't take alcohol – never could. Last time I had alcohol was …' Hilda didn't want to remember.

It was the night Rose was conceived. She had known it had happened the moment Bill had shuddered inside her; the moment he'd become limp; the moment he'd rolled over and left her lying in a damp patch and snored in her ear.

Mary frowned as she concentrated on the narrow road she was driving down.

'I thought I knew this area like the back of my hand. John and I used to take walking holidays round here when we were students.'

She stopped the car to look at her map. In the distance they saw an old farmer pitch-forking hay onto a dilapidated truck. 'Let's ask him the way.'

The women got out of the Austin and walked towards the old man who was talking animatedly to himself; a large hairy wart on the end of his nose wobbled up and down. He carried on pitch-forking as if they weren't there.

'Excuse me – we're looking for the village of Benington and seem to have lost our way. Can you head us in the right direction, please?' Mary asked him.

'Perhaps he's deaf, Mary.' Hilda shouted to the old man, 'We're looking for Benington. Four miles from Stevenage. Can you tell us where it is?'

'Shoutin' won't get you what you be looking for. Benington, is it? Well now.' He scratched his head before looking at the women, then stuck his pitch-fork deep into the earth. 'Benington, you say?' His toothless mouth held all the charm of a deflated punch-bag as he munched his words.

Mary lifted her eyebrows as she looked at Hilda.

'Benington be a long ways from 'ere.'

'Yes, we know that, but if you could just point us in the right direction.'

'Ahh – the right direction, is it? … Well, now.' He scratched his head again and looked around as if searching for a signpost. He suddenly thrust out a rigid arm.

'Turn up that there road, past the Dornier, second left at the Junkers and right after the Heinkel and there be Benington.' The old man snorted with laughter.

Hilda's face flamed. 'What's the matter with you? – just tell us where it is!'

The man stopped laughing and a crafty look crossed his face.

'And why should I be doin' that in wartime. You could be spies for all I knows.'

'Oh, don't be ridiculous,' Hilda shouted. 'Do we look like spies?'

'Course you don't. That be the secret of a spy.' The old man touched the wart on the end of his nose several times before he walked off, whistling to himself, with his pitch-fork over his shoulder.

'Silly old codger!' Hilda shouted after him. 'I could hit him over the head with his bloody pitch-fork.'

'But we could be the perfect Sussex spies, Hilda.'

The women looked at each other for a moment, then suddenly convulsed with laughter.

An hour later, after asking another less suspicious farmer, they found themselves on the road to Benington which Mary knew well. As they were driving along they heard a distant drone in the sky. 'Spitfires!' they cried simultaneously.

Mary stopped the car and the women jumped out.

'Here, Hilda.' Mary gave her a large handkerchief.

They watched the Spitfires approaching and waved white handkerchiefs as the planes flew low over their heads. The young faces of the pilots smiled down at them from the cockpit.

'Charlie was right, Hilda. You can see the colour of their eyes. I didn't believe him.'

As they got back into the car Mary turned to find Hilda crying.

'They've got the best machines in the world, Hilda. They're going to be all right. I know.'

Hilda wiped her eyes with the handkerchief. 'Wish I did, Mary. I don't know what I'd do if –'

'Come on, Hilda, you don't want Rose to see your face all puffy, do you? We'll be there soon.'

Mary started the car and they set off down the road again, the sunlight slanting intermittently onto Mary's new powder-blue dress as they passed row after row of tall ash trees.

'At least we don't look like scarecrows any more,' Mary commented.

Hilda fidgeted in her seat, not comfortable in her sister's clothes. She and Jeannie were both big women, but big in different places. Jeannie's hips were lower than hers. Still, it had been good of her to bring the dress to the hotel after the raid. Mary, of course, had brought her ration book and had enough money to go shopping in the Strand. Hilda looked at Mary's elegant figure, confidently driving along the country lanes. Everything Mary wore looked as if it had been designed just for her, Hilda thought. She looked down at the faded, ill-fitting dress she was wearing. Nothing she wore ever looked as if it had been made for her. Even when it had.

Hilda got out her compact and powdered her nose. In the uncompromising sunshine she saw her wrinkles etching a corrugated map across her face. 'Oh dear, wish I hadn't bothered, Mary. I'm getting allergic to mirrors.'

'Oh, getting old doesn't worry me. Only getting infirm.'

'Well, you're living with the right man, dear, if you become ill.'

Mary laughed. 'I suppose I am … I suppose I'm lucky.'

'I should say so,' said Hilda with more feeling than she'd intended.

Mary looked at her quickly. 'You're not very happily married, are you?'

Hilda looked intently at the road in front of them.

'It's that obvious, is it?'

'Only since I've got to know you better.'

There was a long silence. Hilda didn't know whether she could speak about the things she had only ever thought of before.

'Well, it's my fault, isn't it? I shouldn't have married him.'

'Why did you?'

Hilda tried to remember. Had she ever been in love with Bill? She remembered Kate's face when she'd heard that Rob was home. No. She'd never felt the emotions she'd seen on her daughter's face that day. That glow.

'I don't know, Mary.'

'How did you meet?'

Hilda turned to look at Mary's strong profile; her unlined face. She was still a beautiful woman. Not like me, Hilda thought: fat and frumpy. Could she tell her?

'He was one of the gardeners at Lord and Lady Brassey's mansion in Catsfield like my Dad. What a place that was. My Dad first took me to the big house to see the gardens when I was eight. I couldn't believe that one family lived in such an enormous house. It was surrounded by acres of grass. There was a big grass-cutting machine on the lawn, pulled by a pony that wore leather boots. Can you imagine?' Hilda smiled at the memory. 'When Lady Brassy walked through the open French windows at the back of the mansion, my Dad snapped his cap off and whispered to me:

"That's her Ladyship, Hilda. Don't forget the curtsey Mum learnt you when she walks by. '"Good Morning, your Ladyship. Lovely morning,"' my Dad said. And I didn't forget. I curtsied beautifully on the long sloping lawn which led down to a lake. And then Lady Brassey swept past us, covered from neck to ankle in a flowing white dress. I remember she was carrying a gardening basket in one hand and a long pair of scissors in the other. I said to my Dad, "What's she carrying those for, Dad?" And my Dad answered, "Her Ladyship likes flowers in every room. She cuts them and arranges them herself. Every day." And I looked up at the hundreds of windows and I thought Lady Brassey must spend every hour of the day picking flowers to fill that many rooms. And when I turned round, Mary – I'll never forget it – there was Lord Brassey, staring out at the lake by the French windows, dressed in a starched white linen shirt and black breeches and pearl-covered spats over shining boots. I'd never seen anything so grand.'

Mary stopped the car. There was silence for a few moments, then Hilda turned to find Mary staring at her. She coloured with embarrassment.

'I went to work there as a maid when I was thirteen. Bill started work as an under-gardener at the same time.'

'At thirteen?' Mary said, in astonishment.

'Yes, everyone left school at thirteen in my village then.' Hilda sounded defensive.

'Isn't life strange, Hilda? My parents met Lord and Lady Brassey in 1913, just before the Great War. They went to a cocktail party at Normanshurst.'

'Oh,' said Hilda, colouring even more as she thought about the difference in their backgrounds.

'They were way out of their depth. The Brassey Mansion was far too splendid and the other guests far too wealthy. Lord Brassey spent the evening talking about fox-hunting with the men, and all the women were left to amuse themselves. Daddy told me that he'd had the "honour" of being invited to join the East Sussex Hunt. But when he'd explained the reasons why he was opposed to fox-hunting, he suddenly found himself in an empty room. They were never invited again.'

Hilda looked at Mary 'So your parents went as guests and I went as a servant.'

'They only went once, Hilda. My mother said she felt sorry for Lady Brassey. By 1919, both her husband and son were dead. Wealth isn't everything.'

'But it helps though, doesn't it? My Mum had to take in washing to help feed us before she died giving birth to a little boy.'

'How old was she?' Mary asked in a tight voice.

'Twenty-eight. She had complications and we didn't have any money to call in the doctor. The baby died too. Just as well. I couldn't have looked after him and my Dad and sister.'

Mary breathed deeply. 'You make me feel so guilty.'

Hilda looked at her in surprise. 'What for?'

'Having an easy life.'

'But why? It's fate, isn't it? Fate shuffles the cards and we play them.'

'No. I believe we make our own fate, Hilda. If you believe that, it means you can never step outside a role fate has laid down for you.'

'Well, I can't. I can't go back and have an education now, can I?' Hilda stared at a birch tree at the side of the road, lacquered with a silver glaze.

'No, but look what you've done with your children. All of them have an education and I'm sure that's because of you. You've reshuffled the cards, my dear.' Mary pressed Hilda's hand before starting the car.

Hilda looked at her quickly. 'I never thought of it like that.'

'You've got such a lot to be proud of. It must be wonderful having a grown-up daughter like Kate. There's so many things women can talk about that they can't with men, aren't there? I do like Kate. Rob brought her to our house a couple of times. She's very quiet, but I thought her quite lovely.'

'Quiet? Lovely?' Hilda snorted.

Mary was startled by the vehemence in Hilda's voice.

'She's taken you in, Mary. You don't know her like I do. She's wilful. Always wants her own way and God help anyone who stands in it.'

Mary shivered. She'd always been happy about Rob going out with Kate. 'Really? She didn't seem like that at all.'

Mary was quiet as she drove into the small, beautiful village of Benington fifteen minutes later. She recognized it immediately. She and John had stayed at *The Bell* before Rob was born. It was exactly the same. She stopped the car near the half-timbered cottages spread out by the village green and they got out.

'There it is, Hilda.'

Across the road they saw the large 17th century Rectory. 'Oh dear, it looks a bit grand for my Rose, Mary.'

'Of course it's not. Come on. I'm longing to see her face when she finds us here.'

They walked towards the impressive two-storeyed porch. Mary rang the old black bell which echoed throughout the house. Hilda thought her heart was going to burst out of her chest as she waited to see her little girl.

No one came.

'Don't say we've come all this way and they're out. I can't bear it.' Hilda was close to tears.

'Don't be silly, we'll find them. It's only a small village. Let's go over to *The Bell*. Pubs know everything about everyone in a village, don't they?'

They tripped over the uneven surface of the path towards the pub and Hilda was back on the unmade roads of Catsfield with their clouds of childhood summer dust. She had almost forgotten how bad unpaved roads were after living in a town for so long.

The noise in the pub gradually diminished as the men looked up at the unfamiliar sight of two women walking into their territory.

Hilda had never been into a pub without Bill before. Her face was the colour of beetroot.

'Afternoon, ladies. What can I be doing you for?' joked the landlord.

Mary ignored the innuendo and smiled. 'We're looking for the vicar of St Peter's. He doesn't seem to be at home.'

The men looked at each other, startled.

'And who might you be?' the landlord asked.

'We've got children evacuated here. Mrs Brazier's daughter is staying with the vicar.'

'Oh dear, oh dear, oh dear,' the landlord rubbed his chin in agitation.

'What's the matter?' Hilda clenched her fingers over the pub counter.

'The little girl what was staying with the Reverend and his sisters disappeared yesterday and so did a boy from Bert Ackroyd's farm. We been looking for them.'

Hilda saw the publican sway. The next moment, she was looking up from the pub floor to find a circle of faces staring down at her. She struggled to sit up.

'Take it slowly, Hilda,' Mary said.

Then she started to cry. Small sobs at first, until gradually her whole body shook with the enormity of her fears; her terror anchored in the stomachs of all the men in the pub. They sat down, stunned.

They were sitting in the drawing room of the Rectory after finding the vicar and his sisters in church, praying for Rose's soul. The vicar looked at Hilda as if life was too complicated for him to comprehend. His sisters fluttered around the room, unable to sit down.

'We did everything we could to help Rose settle in, Mrs Brazier,' Miss Elizabeth said.

'We thought she had settled in well, didn't we, Algie?' Miss Margaret said to her brother. The vicar nodded vaguely; his mind on higher things.

'She's been singing in the choir for weeks – like an angel, everyone said. Such a good little girl, we hardly knew she was here, did we, Algie?' The vicar nodded again.

'You are talking about my Rose, aren't you?' Hilda was bemused by their description and brought out a photograph from her handbag. She gave it to the vicar who nodded and passed it to his sisters.

'Oh yes, that's Rose. As I said, such a quiet child. We can't understand why she'd run away.'

The vicar seemed unaware of the fact that he was pulling tufts of horsehair out of his armchair onto the worn Turkish carpet as he contemplated Genesis.

Hilda took back the photograph of Rose and put in her handbag. She could see her rigid figure reflected in the numerous glass-fronted display cabinets, full of porcelain china, which decorated the room.

'When did you last see her?' Mary asked the sisters, realising that they wouldn't achieve anything by asking the vicar questions. He seemed to be sitting on the periphery of this world, waiting to be transported into the next, Mary thought, looking at him absent-mindedly picking the chair to pieces.

'Yesterday morning,' Miss Margaret said, looking at her sister. 'Wasn't it, Elizabeth? – just before we went to the church, about 11 o'clock.'

'And no one in the village saw Rose at all?'

'No, that's the odd thing, Mrs – ?'

'Adams,' Mary said, trying to keep her mind focused on the room and not what was happening to Charlie and Rose.

'She said she was going to pick some honeysuckle from the garden. We do all the flower arrangements in the church you know and Rose came with us every day.'

'Every day!' Hilda couldn't believe it. Rose had only ever been in church twice in her life before leaving home.

'Well, of course. We all go to church every day, don't we, Algie?'

The vicar nodded. The tufts of horsehair were growing into a small mountain around his feet.

'I do wish you wouldn't do that, dear. It's not doing the chair any good and it was mother's favourite,' said Miss Elizabeth, looking at her brother. He stopped immediately and put the palms of his hands together as if praying for peace.

'Where's the police station?' Mary asked.

Everyone looked at her in alarm.

'Police?' murmured the vicar, greatly agitated. 'No, that won't do, that won't do, at all. I'm not having any police here. I've got a sermon to write. I must have peace and quiet.'

The sisters stared at Mary. 'Of course, you must, Algie, dear. As if we'd invite the police into the house.' Miss Elizabeth turned to Mary coldly. 'Why do you need to talk to the police?'

'Well, nobody seems to have seen the children, do they? We must inform them.'

Hilda let out a large groan and the vicar's face became ashen.

'I must go to my study. Excuse me.' He scurried out of the room.

'Oh dear,' said Miss Elizabeth. 'I do hope these events haven't disturbed Algie too much. He has so much to think about with the Harvest Festival drawing near.'

Mary looked at Hilda's pained expression. 'I'm only talking to the police as a precaution, that's all, Hilda. We've got to explore every avenue we can.' She turned to the sisters. 'Did Rose have any favourite walks around here?'

The sisters looked at each other blankly. 'Walks? We haven't any time for walking.'

'I mean Rose, not you.'

'We certainly wouldn't allow a child out by itself, Mrs Adams. That would be irresponsible, wouldn't it?'

Hilda got up abruptly. 'I want to go, Mary. Come on.'

The sisters looked at each other and frowned.

'Well … thank you for your help,' Mary said, standing up.

'I see,' said Miss Elizabeth, not quite knowing what to do. 'I do hope you find Rose. Such a nice child.'

There was a short silence, then Hilda suddenly ran towards the door and out of the house.

'Well, really,' Miss Margaret said. 'She hasn't even taken Rose's things.'

Mary looked at her in amazement. 'You've packed her things already?'

'Well, of course, it's obvious the child didn't want to stay here, Mrs Adams, and we don't want a child in the house who doesn't want to stay. Her case is by the door … '

Miss Margaret rang a small silver bell on a small silver tray and Mabel hobbled into the room from the kitchen.

'Mabel will show you out, Mrs Adams. You will excuse us. It's been a most tiring day.'

Mary breathed deeply before striding rapidly past the old servant and the two sisters into the large gloomy hall. She picked up Rose's case and slammed the heavy 17th century Rectory door hard behind her.

The two sisters' faces registered shocked disbelief; their rigid observance of protocol having more in common with Jane Austen's world than the 20th century.

'Well really, those women have no manners, Elizabeth.'

'Unbelievable, Margaret, absolutely no manners at all.'

And they nodded slowly in perfect harmony.

Mary found Hilda sobbing in the car and put her arms around her.

'They'll be all right, Hilda. Rose is with Charlie. Remember what that man said in the pub?'

Hilda shook her head. The only thing she had heard was Rose had disappeared.

'He said Rose had gone and also a boy from Bert Ackroyd's farm. Charlie will look after Rose. Remember, he gave you a solemn promise?'

Hilda's face was puffy with crying. She blew her nose loudly and looked at Mary.

'He did, didn't he? They've gone together, haven't they? But where've they gone, Mary?'

Mary sat back in the seat, feeling emotionally and physically drained.

'I don't know, Hilda. We'll have to think. You wait here and I'll go to the police station.'

Hilda's face flooded with fear again.

'I just think the police can ring around the countryside and find out if any one has seen two children far quicker than we can.'

'Yes, you're right as usual, Mary. I don't know what I would have done without you in that Rectory.'

'That place is living proof that religion's in the heart, Hilda – not the knees. I'll be back soon.'

Hilda watched Mary's elegant figure walking down the road towards the police station and tried not to think of all the dangers Rose could be facing.

Ten minutes later, Mary was driving them down the dirt track towards Bert Ackroyd's farm.

'The police haven't any leads, but the Ackroyds might, Hilda.'

Mary stopped outside the front door of the farmhouse and was assaulted by the same smell of manure that Charlie couldn't first identify. The women got out of the car, glad to stretch their legs, and looked around. The farm seemed deserted.

'Hallo!' Mary shouted.

In the distance, they saw a tall old man with long white hair blowing around in the wind like cotton. He walked across a field towards them. They waved to him. He waved back.

'Thank goodness, someone's here.'

'Well, he can certainly move, can't he?' Hilda said, as they watched Grandfer walk briskly into the farmyard. They smiled at him.

'Hello, I'm Mrs Adams, Charlie's … mother. Could you tell us –'

'Parnips,' mouthed Grandfer, walking straight past them to the vegetable garden; his long root-like fingers itching to tear something out of the ground.

'Pardon?'

'Parnips needs pullin'.'

The women looked at each other in astonishment as he disappeared.

'Mad as a hatter,' Mary said. 'Let's knock on the door. Someone might be in.'

They saw the sudden movement of a shadow in an upstairs window.

'Someone's there, Mary.'

Hilda banged on the door loudly. No one came. She banged again.

'Well, we're not going until we find out who it is.' Hilda was becoming angry.

She pushed the front door open. Suddenly they heard a voice behind them.

'And what you think you're doin'?'

They both jumped, colouring with embarrassment.

'I'm sorry,' Mary said. ` But we've been knocking for ages. We knew someone was in – we saw them upstairs.'

Alice Ackroyd knew who Mary was. She had seen a picture of her, hidden in Charlie's letters. She had also seen what was written on the back. *Lots of Love from Auntie Mary.*

'What d'you want?' The animosity on the woman's face shocked Mary.

'I'm Mrs Adams, Charlie's … mother.'

They waited for the woman to say something. She didn't.

'We've just found out from the village that he's disappeared with my friend's daughter.' She motioned towards Hilda.

'We've driven up from London to see them both.'

Mary looked at Hilda. Alice Ackroyd was still staring at them, almost malevolently.

'Excuse me, could you speak to us, please.' Hilda shouted at the woman. 'We're trying to find our children.'

'Don't you shout at me! I don't know nothing,' she turned to Mary, 'except that boy you calls your son near killed mine couple of days back.'

'What?' Mary looked at the small woman in horror. 'What do you mean?'

'What I seez. Tried to strangle him.' The sound of a tractor cut across her words. 'Ask Mr Ackroyd if you don't believe us.'

Bert Ackroyd climbed out of his tractor slowly. He was tired. He'd been out trying to find where Charlie had gone. He put out a mud-spattered arm to shake Mary and Hilda's hand.

'Excuse the dirt. Been busy on the farm. You'll be Charlie's Mum. Sorry business … running off like that.'

'Mr Ackroyd. Is it true what this … lady just told me?'

Bert looked at his wife quickly. 'About Charlie trying to strangle Daniel? 'Fraid it is.'

'He's got the marks on his neck an all,' Alice Ackroyd snapped. 'Can hardly speak.'

Mary looked up to see a boy looking down at them from an upstairs window. He suddenly darted out of sight.

'Can I talk to him?'

'Why?'

'To find out why Charlie did it, of course. He's not violent.'

Alice snorted. 'Not violent! I call strangling someone violent.'

'But he didn't strangle him, did he? He ran away and I want to find out why.'

'You'd best come in,' Bert said.

'Wipe your feet first,' the woman snapped.

They walked into the dark kitchen, gradually distinguishing the black china cats with glowing green eyes sitting ominously on the mantelpiece. Then Mary noticed Charlie's suitcase lying open on the floor and his belongings ransacked. The woman followed Mary's gaze and sniffed as she sat down in her rocking chair.

'Sit down, won't you,' Bert said. He walked over to the stairs.

'Daniel. Come down here.'

'Do I have to, Pa?' the boy shouted.

'You do,' Bert shouted back.

They all sat in silence as the boy walked down the stairs, his neck wrapped in a long, white cloth. Mary didn't like the eyes that stared at her out of the boy's pimply face. They were furtive.

'Can you tell me why Charlie attacked you? I'm … his mother.'

'Dunno, do I? I was minding me own business when he comes at me like a bull and done this.'

The boy walked towards Mary, almost triumphantly, and showed her the purple bruises on his neck.

'See?' he smirked at her.

Mary could smell his strong body odour. Everything about him reeked of deceit. She was shocked by her desire to slap him hard across the face.

'That boy of yours'll be locked up afore he's much older, mark m'words. Born little savage, doing that to Daniel. We could have gone to the police, you know.'

'Why didn't you, then?' Mary was alarmed by the anger that was rising inside her.

'No need for that, Alice. Over now, and Charlie was a good little worker, except for the milking.'

Mary looked at him. 'What work?'

Bert was taken aback. 'The work on the farm. Herding and planting and collecting the fruit and the like.'

'But he wasn't sent here to work, Mr Ackroyd. He's only eleven. We sent you money every week for his keep.' Mary was really angry now. 'And how many hours did he work?'

'Same as the rest of us!' Alice Ackroyd shot out of the chair. 'Some of us have to work for money, you know.'

Mary could feel herself shaking. 'And some people, Mrs Ackroyd, obviously don't know that it's a criminal offence to employ children to do a man's job.'

Alice looked quickly at her husband.

Mary rushed over to get Charlie's case and found it had been slashed with a knife.

'He done that afore he left. Told you – a born savage.'

Hilda put her arm on Mary's shoulder. She could feel her trembling.

'Are all his clothes there, Mary?'

'No.'

Hilda turned to Bert Ackroyd. 'Could we have the rest of Charlie's clothes, please?'

'I'll get them from his room.'

Mary closed Charlie's case and walked out of the house.

'We'll be outside,' Hilda shouted up the stairs to him.

Mary stood in the yard looking at the fields, breathing deeply.

'You all right, Mary?'

She shook her head.

Bert Ackroyd came out of the house, carrying a couple of Charlie's shirts and short trousers Mary had bought him before he'd left.

'That's all I could find.'

Mary got in the car.

'Thank you, Mr Ackroyd,' Hilda said. 'She's a bit upset.'

'Well, sorry it had to end like this … you know … hope you find Charlie all right and your daughter.'

'Yes,' Hilda said, getting into the car.

Mary drove off almost before Hilda had time to close the door.

Chapter 29

'My body grows lean in the hunger of my loneliness.'

James Carlisle
The Feather Bed, 1906

A roar of laughter hit Rob the moment he opened the heavy green and yellow door of Shepherd's pub in Mayfair: the unofficial home of Fighter Command pilots. Here they could catch up on all the news of friends from Oscar, the short, dark Swiss publican who ran the pub with military precision. He was leaning over the bar talking to a group of Canadian fighter-pilots from 242 Squadron, dressed in his usual black coat and immaculate grey striped trousers.

'Oh yes, I know Squadron Leader Bader. Strong ideas, but I cannot agree with his Big Wing,' Oscar said in his clipped European accent.

'Pint of your best watered-down beer please, Oscar.'

Oscar's face froze as he turned towards the person who had brought his integrity into disrepute.

Rob gave him his devastating lop-sided smile and Oscar's small dark face broke into a beam. 'Robert! – I might have known. Oh, you English – so good at serious jokes.'

He left the Canadians to fend for themselves as he got Rob a drink and waved him over to one of the alcoves in the corner of the rectangular room. 'I bring it to you.'

Rob smiled as he glanced around at the crowded pub, decorated in a Regency style. Exactly the same. He remembered a wonderful evening with Colin and some other pilots, singing bawdy songs around Oscar's old piano. God! Suddenly Rob's smile faded. One of them had been Peter Rawlins. He'd crashed two weeks later and died three days before his twenty-first birthday. Rob's hands shook slightly as he lit a cigarette.

Through the smoke, he saw a number of pretty young women, dressed in frocks which barely skimmed their knees. Hemlines seemed to be getting shorter all the time, he thought. They were sitting on small seats underneath the pub's mullion bay windows and leaned forward to stare at him. They smiled. He smiled slowly back, the left corner of his mouth crinkling his cheek. They widened their eyes and moved their legs imperceptibly so that their skirts shifted to a higher plane.

Oscar looked at the women looking at Rob as he walked over with his pint of beer. 'My God – what you do to women, Robert? Why can't I do it, hmm?' He sat down beside him. 'That smile of yours. It even gets George excited and he's a happily married man!'

Rob laughed as George, the lounge waiter, walked past carrying a tray of beers. It wobbled wildly as he glanced across to see Rob sitting with Oscar. 'Hello, Sir – nice to see you again!' he shouted.

'Be careful with the drinks, George,' Oscar called, wiping his forehead. Laughter was all very well, he thought, as long as it didn't interfere with business.

Rob waved to George and then suddenly leaned his head back against the alcove wall, feeling drained. Oscar looked at him.

'Ah, I have seen that look so many times, Robert, you cannot imagine. They expect too much from you young pilots. Having to always learn new tactics in the air. A man can only do what a man can do, I always say.'

'Well, the RAF thinks we can do a lot, Oscar.'

'I know, I know … Oh before I forget – Hugh Dundas was here last week and sent his – what was the expression? – his regards. You English have some odd expressions. He too is a Flying Officer now … Ah yes – you know who I was talking to the other day – CO Malan from 74 Squadron. The South African. You know him?'

Rob nodded. He'd met him on a course six months ago when Malan was a Flight Commander. If anyone hated Germans, it was him.

'He said to me, "you know, Oscar. I think it's better to send a German plane home crippled than to shoot it down – with a dead rear gunner, a dead navigator and a pilot coughing up his lungs as he lands. It lowers their morale." Such violence in one man. My God.'

'Well, we are at war, Oscar.'

'Yes, I know, Robert, but surely there can be a little honour?'

Rob looked at him for some time. 'That's an interesting idea, perhaps you should talk to Hitler about it.'

'God forbid that he should walk into my pub.'

Rob laughed loudly at the thought. 'Well – I want to forget war for a while. I've come to enjoy myself.'

'In London? – with the raids? An odd choice.' Oscar's eyebrows almost reached the top of his head. 'How long have you got?'

'Forty-eight hours.'

Oscar made a dismissive gesture with his hands and mouth. 'Forty-eight hours! I could not even make a good Swiss cheese in the time. You need a week.'

'I need a month, Oscar, but I've only got forty-eight hours and I've got to see someone tomorrow so that only leaves tonight.'

'Ah – another lady, I think.'

Rob smiled. 'There's only one in my life now.' He drew out a photograph of Kate and gave it to Oscar. Her clear blue eyes and beautiful chestnut hair radiated from it.

'Ahh,' Oscar sighed his appreciation. 'The Chinese have a saying: "a wife is sought for her virtue, a concubine for her beauty." Your lady is certainly beautiful …' He spread his arms in a revelatory gesture as he got up, looking into Rob's startled brown eyes.

'Enjoy your evening, Robert.' He pointed to Rob's beer. 'That "watered-down" beer is, as you say, on me.'

Rob frowned as he watched Oscar's dapper, but distinguished figure, weaving expertly in and out of the chain of pilots who were passing pints of beer to each other. He drank deeply, thinking about what Oscar had said. He knew Kate was a virgin. It had been his disastrous idea to take her to that boarding-house. He shuddered as he remembered the experience. It was his fault that he'd wanted a perfect experience and had taken her to an imperfect place; it was his fault that he hadn't been able to explain his coldness to her; he hadn't wanted the vulnerability of love in wartime.

He drank the rest of his beer and looked up to find a short woman standing in front of him wearing a red, tight dress and heavy make-up. There was no mistaking her purpose. She sat down beside him crossing her legs high to reveal a large amount of heavy thigh.

'Ohh, I love a good fighter, luv. Always takin' risks … know what I mean.' She pressed stumpy fingers into his thigh.

'Don't do that.' Rob's voice was glacial as he stood up, pushing the woman's fingers away.

'Ohh – sorry I'm sure. Didn't knows you was Royalty, luv.'

Rob walked through a crowd of pilots who were enjoying the exchange.

'Charges more for 'em!' the woman shouted after him.

The pilots roared with laughter.

Rob walked over to the other side of the room, hating the crimson colour flooding his face. Why couldn't he be like Colin? He'd have been chatting to the woman by now and suggesting they go to her place. Why couldn't he? What did it matter? How long had he got, anyway?

He looked around for a familiar face. There weren't any. The pilots all seemed to belong to the same squadron: their spontaneous bursts of laughter excluding outsiders. And suddenly, the night stretched endlessly in front of him. He ordered a whisky from a new bartender. In the distance, he could see Oscar gesticulating the evening orders to George. He obviously had no more time to talk.

He moved back, away from the crowd, and knocked over a drink that someone had left on the floor. It spread a dark brown pool across Oscar's carpet.

'I've just bought that.'

A tall, lean girl bent down to pick up the glass. She stood up and examined Rob's features, then lifted a hand to sweep a halo of frizzy brown hair from her face.

'Sorry – didn't see it.'

'Well, obviously – I didn't think you'd knock it over on purpose. It's bacardi and coke.'

Rob looked at her for some time. 'Pardon?'

'The drink you spilt – barcardi and coke. It cost 9d.'

Rob stared down at the empty glass she put in his hand.

'You're very direct.'

'It's the best way to get what you want, isn't it?'

She had a wide, open smile which crinkled up her large blue-grey eyes. Rob found himself smiling back. There was something very refreshing about her.

An hour later, Rob was still talking to the girl, telling her about his home, his friends, his flying. He knew hardly anything about her, except her name. Billie. She reminded him of Charlie the way she kept asking him questions.

'You know something – you ought to be in RAF Intelligence.' Rob was suddenly worried, wondering if he'd said too much about the squadron. 'You've had more information out of me in an hour than most people have in a lifetime ... what about your life?'

'Oh, I'm not interesting – other people's lives are far more sparkling than mine. I'm only a secretary in the City. Nothing exciting like flying.' Her eyes traced the outline of Rob's face. 'Let's go to the *Cafe de Paris* in Coventry Street. It's only a hop by taxi.'

Rob looked at her in surprise. 'I've never met anyone – apart from …' He waved in the direction of the prostitutes who were chatting up the pilots.

'So direct,' she interrupted, smiling. 'Yes, you keep saying. Haven't you noticed, things have changed since the war started? Come on, they've got some great bands playing.'

Billie got them a taxi immediately. As they drove through the streets of London, Rob was stunned by the devastation he could see around him. He'd travelled by underground to the pub. Over the last few months, he had spent his time either flying over the smoke of London or sleeping. His brief aerial views had not prepared him for the piles of bricks and mortar lying in the streets, or the sight of blackened shells which had once been buildings.

'Heard about the unexploded bomb in St Pauls?' The cab driver said, weaving an intricate path through the bomb craters which pitted the roads. 'Me brother's in the Royal Engineers. Bomb disposal. Don't know how he does it, meself. Bleedin' terrify me it would. Had to slow right down when we was drivin' near it in case the vibration set it off. Not that I did, mind you. Bleedin' terrified. Me brother said that this Lieutenant what's his name – Davies – that's it – tried to have the bomb lifted with 'em hawsers – three times and the bleedin' thing kept droppin. Stuff of nightmares, init? Closed all the roads through the East End they did and all the houses had to be evacuated. You should have heard me Aunt Dolly's language when this geezer told her. This Lieutenant what's his name – Canadian, me brother said – bleedin' hero, he was – I tell you – put this bomb on a lorry packed with cushions and that and then he drove it – by hisself, mind you, through the East End to Hackney Marshes – through all the bleedin' red traffic lights an' all and had it exploded. You know how big the crater was? Hundred foot across. Hundred foot, mind you … Where'd you want to go again?'

The small dance-floor was heaving by the time they arrived at the underground club, beneath the Rialto Cinema in Coventry Street. It was advertised as the safest club in town. Ken 'Slippery' Johnson and his Caribbean band were playing a Calypso as they were shown to a table. The room was dimly lit by candlelight.

'I love this music, don't you?' Billie said, dragging Rob onto the dance floor. She moved like a snake to the music. Rob had never seen anyone dance like that before and stood in front of her in amazement, not knowing what to do.

'Come on, Rob – relax into the music.'

He was mesmerized by the movement of her hips. They didn't seem to be connected to her body at all. She took his hands and showed him how to move and suddenly he was laughing. He realised it didn't matter what he did. He could just enjoy himself.

'It's wizard,' he shouted over the music.

She pulled a face at him. 'What?'

'Sorry – RAF jargon.' Rob found he was just getting into the swing of the music when it stopped and the dance floor miraculously emptied. He stood there laughing.

'You're an amazing girl, you know.'

'Yes, I know … come on.' She took his hand and pulled him towards the table. 'I need a drink.'

Two dances later, the air was distorted by the shrill sound of feedback from the band's microphone. A mechanic adjusted the sound as 'Slippery' Johnson started to speak.

'Ladies and Gentlemen. We have a surprise for you tonight. I can see the lovely Billie Stuart in the audience. Come on up here, Billie, and give us a song.'

Suddenly a spotlight lit up Billie's halo of frizzy hair and people started clapping. Rob's mouth fell open as he realised they all knew her.

'I'm resting, tonight, Slips.'

'Ah c'mon – just one, Billie.'

People started a slow hand-clap and Billie got up laughing and put up her hands.

'Okay – but only one.'

Rob sat there, stunned, as Billie walked over and picked up the microphone as if she'd been born with it in her hand. She turned to the band.

'Baby Doll.'

People started whistling and stomping on the floor. The band broke into the first eight bars and everyone fell silent as Billie began singing in a surprisingly deep, rich, erotic voice. As she sang "I wanna be somebody's Baby Doll so I can get my loving all the time," her eyes never moved from Rob's face and he found his body responding in a way it never had before. Jesus, he thought, where'd she learnt to breathe like that. She didn't sing notes, she seduced them.

The audience went wild, whooping and clapping, as the last note died on her lips. Rob found himself going wild too. He wanted to take her on the table in front of everyone. She walked slowly towards him, swinging her hips just enough to be interesting. All the men in the room followed their movement as she sat down opposite him.

'You told me you were a secretary,' Rob said, loosening his tie. He was finding breathing difficult.

'I am – in the day. In the night – I do other things.' She was looking at him with an expression he couldn't understand.

'I've never heard anyone sing like that.'

'Then you've never heard Bessie Smith sing. Come on – let's go.'

Rob followed her without a murmur, while the band and crowd shouted out for her to stay. She turned and waved at them as she walked out.

The second taxi-driver was no relation to the first; he was mute all the way to Bloomsbury Square. Bloomsbury Square! How on earth could a secretary afford a place here, Rob thought, as they drew up in front of a palatial Georgian white house.

They got out and Billie ran up the steps to open an enormous dark-blue door as Rob paid for the taxi. He followed her into a large hall.

'You live here?' He was completely overawed by the evident signs of wealth. The enormous white hall was full of what looked like Chippendale furniture.

Billie grinned at him. 'It's Daddy's house – not mine.'

'God – he's not here?' The last thing Rob wanted to do was to meet an irate father at this time of night. He was beginning to think he'd been mad to come to London to enjoy himself.

She laughed at his expression. 'Don't worry. He's abroad and the few servants we have left have gone home.'

'Servants!'

'Come on – I'll show you my bedroom.'

Rob could feel his heart thump hard against his rib cage as he followed Billie's swaying hips up the wide sweeping staircase; their feet making no sound on the expensive deep blue carpet.

Rob walked into the biggest bedroom he had ever seen. It must have been over twenty-six foot square. Astonishment spread across his face as he looked around at the expensive furnishings; it was like a Hollywood film set. His feet felt the springy deep pile of the cream carpet which covered the entire floor. Along one wall was a gigantic four-poster bed covered in elegant damask drapes: seven foot long, seven foot wide, and on the walls, the largest and strangest paintings he had ever seen. He walked across the room and stood in front of one of them: the figure of a man with a skull-head and a wheel-barrel seemingly growing out of it was facing a woman with a large stick, seemingly growing out of her back. It was like trying to read a secret code.

'*"The Atavism of Dusk"*' Billie said, coming up close to him. 'Dali felt threatened by women, hence the skull. You see how he's made the woman bend in the posture of a praying mantis? The stick coming out of her back represents her sting.'

Rob rubbed his cheek as he walked over towards the ceiling-high windows, draped in damask-coloured curtains to look at another painting. It was called *'The Architectural Angelus of Millet'*. He saw two tall monumental stones set in a surrealistic landscape and shook his head in bewilderment.

'Fascinating, isn't it?' She looked across the room at him. 'You know Dali's work?'

'No.' He couldn't understand why anyone would want to.

'It shows the transformation of Millet's peasants. Both figures have been turned into monumental stones. The tall stone –' she pointed to the large biomorphic shape on the left of the canvas, 'that's the male stone towering over the female stone.'

'But the female seems to be penetrating the male,' Rob said. He could see a large phallic shape protruding from the shorter stone.

Billie looked at him, and smiled. 'Yes, I know.' She linked her arms behind Rob's head and kissed him, her tongue deep in his mouth. He felt he was drowning and pulled away.

'Billie – I don't –'

'Shhh – don't talk.' She took off his uniform with practised fingers and pulled him over to the bed. Rob lay there feeling like an animal silhouetted in searchlights and couldn't move. Her fingers spread sensuously over his penis, across his hips, up his chest, towards his neck. He was erect in a second and reached for her.

'Slow down. We've got all night.' She sat on his stomach, her legs straggling his body and undressed – very, very slowly while he watched.

Rob had never felt so excited by a woman before and sat up, pushing her down onto the bed.

He moved on top of her, kissing her briefly, before he moved down her surprisingly lean, muscular body until he reached the dark tangle of her pubic hair. She moved slightly and threw a switch above the bed and the room was subdued in subtle light as she spread her legs wide for him.

Two hours later, Rob was almost shaking with exhaustion. They'd made love four times, in four different positions, and she still wanted more. He lay back, his body a sheen of sweat as she sang softly to herself, waiting for his next erection. He couldn't believe he'd been so stupid. How the hell was he going to have the energy to drive up to Benington tomorrow to see Charlie. He looked up at *"The Atavism of Dusk"* and knew exactly how Dali had felt when he'd painted it.

His eyes were beginning to close when the room quivered with the rising wail of the siren. Suddenly, the sound of rapid ack-ack fire cracked through the air and they were blinded with meteoric white light. Rob leapt from the bed: a mixture of relief and fear. He no longer had to perform. He rushed to get dressed.

'Oh, not tonight,' Billie moaned.

'Have you got a basement?'

'I never use it.' She rolled over in the bed.

'Well I am. Where is it?'

'I thought fighters were supposed to be reckless.'

'Reckless, not stupid, now come on for Christ's sake!'

Rob could hear the heavy drone of enemy bombers approaching. He could feel the sweat break out again all over his body. This was far worse than fighting in the air – there was nothing he could do to stop them coming.

They ran down the stairs towards the basement just as the square was lit by what looked like the bright red glow of a firework. Suddenly, there was a violent explosion; they both hung onto the banisters, transfixed as the whole house swayed from side to side as if being shaken by a giant's hand. Rob couldn't believe what he was seeing. It was terrifying. The windows bulged outwards; there was the sudden shatter of glass and thousands of fragments hurled themselves around the house, slicing through paintings and curtains and carpets. Furniture slid across the hall and smashed into walls, clouds of plaster and dust swirled in columns and choked their lungs. Then silence. Billie lay, spread-eagled across the stairs, her head bleeding, her eyes closed. She was covered in thousands of tiny glass fragments. Rob sat up, touching his body in amazement, coughing to clear the dust from his lungs. He hadn't been hurt by the glass at all. He crunched down the stairs, picking his way carefully through the glass towards her, and touched her with trembling fingers.

'Billie?' He got a handkerchief and wiped away the blood on her head. 'Billie? For God's sake, are you all right?' He shook her gently.

She suddenly opened her eyes and smiled at him. 'You don't think the Germans are going to stop our night of passion, do you?'

'Oh, thank God,' Rob said, laughing with relief. 'It must take at least two squadrons of bombers to stop you.' He tried to sit her up and she screamed. Warm blood pumped over his hands. Then he looked down. A spear of glass was embedded in her side.

Over the next few hours Rob lived in Dali's surrealism: running through a door which was wide open, bending obliquely from one hinge; seeing dazed people stumbling through shards of ankle-deep glass in the square; hearing the uncontrollable wailing of a mother clutching her limp child under a shrapnelled tree; smelling the acrid burning oil rising from the wreckage of a Junkers bomber which had torn through one of the houses; sobbing in hysterics at the sight of a fire engine and an ambulance lurching around the corner towards the bombed, almost demolished square; dragging ambulance workers into Billie's house. And then, the nightmare drive to the hospital where they fought to keep her alive.

Rob was kept in hospital overnight, suffering from shock. He couldn't sit down, couldn't lie down. Kept talking, talking, talking, until they sedated him.

He woke in a white room and stared at the white ceiling. Suddenly the memories flooded back and he shot up in the bed, screaming. A young VAD appeared out of nowhere. 'Shh – you'll wake the whole hospital.'

'Where's Billie?'

'Is that the girl they brought in with the glass in her side?'

Rob nodded, terrified to look into the nurse's face.

'It's all right – she's out of danger. Thank goodness, the glass didn't penetrate any vital organs.'

Rob lay back in the bed and sobbed – great racking sobs which shook his body. The young VAD didn't know what to do and rushed off to get Sister. After a few minutes Rob became calmer and his eyes began to close.

The door opened abruptly and Rob saw a wavering shape approach his bed.

'I'm Sister Philips. You've been making a lot of noise, young man. Frightened my nurse half out of her wits. What have you to say for yourself?'

'Tell Charlie I can't …' Rob slurred. Soon his snores could be heard in the next room.

Chapter 30

'You can give them your love,
but not your dreams
For children live in the house of tomorrow.'

James Carlisle
The Feather Bed, 1906

Charlie was underground in a tomb, covered with the smell of earth and decay. He found his arms wouldn't work and something was pressing against his mouth: he was suffocating slowly. He had to move his arms before the man came. He opened his mouth to scream and felt earth falling into it.

He woke with the weight of the bivouac on his face. It had partially collapsed in the night. He pushed it away, grinning with relief as he wiped the earth and leaves from his mouth and looked across at Rose. She was curled into a ball and covered with twigs and branches. He shivered in the early morning air and woke her. She blinked at him and started shaking.

'I'm freezing, Charlie.' Tears started to well up in her eyes. 'I want my Mum.'

'Well, she's not here. C'mon.'

Charlie crawled out of the bivouac and saw the mist rising from the forest floor. Growing all around the tall pine trees were hundreds of red-topped mushrooms.

'P'haps we could eat them,' he said, shivering as Rose crawled out after him.

She looked suspiciously at their red-mottled tops and wrapped her arms around her body for warmth.

'Wish my Mum was here. She knows all about mushrooms. Might be poisonous. Nuts are safer.'

Charlie began jumping up and down to stop his teeth from chattering. 'Nuts! – I'm not a bleedin' squirrel.'

The sight of Charlie with twists of leaves and twigs sticking out of his hair and clothes, jumping up and down, was too much for Rose. She started giggling. 'You look like a scarecrow.'

'So do you. C'mon – I'll chase you – get you warm.' He ran towards her but Rose wouldn't budge.

'Don't be daft.'

He pushed her round some trees.

'Stop it, Charlie!'

'Well, run then!'

'Oh, all right.'

The children ran around the trees and along a path until they came to a stream, deep in a cutting. They both stopped to look down at it; their breath coming in short gasps. As their breathing became quieter, they gradually heard it gurgling over a tiny waterfall of stones. Charlie looked at the reflections of the trees in the water.

'We could wash in it, couldn't we?' Rose said.

'What for?' He looked at her in astonishment.

'We're dirty, Charlie.'

Rose clambered down the bank, the wind bringing a yellow shower of aspen and poplar leaves flying over her head. She watched them swirl into the stream as she took off her shoes and socks and walked into the water.

'What you doing that for?'

'I'm washing, Charlie. Lots of people do, you know.' She rubbed her hands and face, then caught some of the leaves floating in the stream and washed her feet with them.

Charlie's mouth fell open and Rose looked up at him and laughed.

'My Mum says if you leave your mouth open, flies will get you.'

'Your Mum says too much.'

She stopped laughing and walked out of the stream.

'Sorry.'

Rose rubbed her feet on the grass. Charlie sat down and watched green stains and brown mud merge into an intricate pattern over them.

'That one of your better ideas, is it?'

'Well, how was I supposed to know, Charlie Slater?'

'Intelligence?'

'Oh yes! – and who failed his 11+?'

Charlie stood up quickly and walked back along the path they'd just taken.

'Sorry.' She called after him. 'Wait for me.'

Charlie didn't answer.

They'd been walking for an hour along a country lane.

'I'm hungry,' Rose whined. 'And my feet are hurting. Can't we stop?'

Charlie turned back to look at her. 'You know what I hate about girls? Always moaning.'

They walked along in silence for some time.

'You do know where we're going, don't you?' she asked him.

'Yeah.'

'Where?'

'Along this lane.'

'Don't be funny. You know what I mean.'

'We're going to see Rob and Colin at Fowlmere, you know that.'

'Yes, but where *is* Fowlmere?' She stopped walking to look into his face. 'You don't know, do you?'

'No.'

'What!' She shouted, running in front of him.

Charlie didn't want her to know that he was worried. The only people they'd seen in forty-eight hours were some farm workers in a distant field.

'Someone's bound to come along here soon,' he said, looking down the lane at some bushes. 'Can we eat those berries?'

Rose looked at the bushes, bursting with thick, juicy blackberries. She could feel the saliva saturate her mouth as she ran towards them.

'Of course, we can. Haven't you seen blackberry bushes before?' she shouted back to him.

'Not many blackberries in our street,' Charlie answered quietly.

But Rose didn't hear. She was pulling the blackberries off the bushes and stuffing them in her mouth: the dark, red juice dripping down her chin.

'Mmm. Taste them, Charlie. They're fantastic.'

Charlie ran up and pulled his first blackberry off a bush and popped it in his mouth. He couldn't believe the flavour that hit his taste buds. 'Blimey. Why didn't you tell me they tasted like this?'

Soon they were racing to see who could pick and eat the most, until their faces and fingers were covered in purple juice.

'That's enough, Charlie.'

'What?'

'Mum says you mustn't eat too many 'cos they give you tummy ache.'

He was about to argue with her when they saw a jeep driving slowly down the dusty lane towards them. They dropped the blackberries they were holding. Rose rushed to get her handkerchief to wipe her hands and face.

'Charlie, we look awful.'

He stood in the middle of the road with his hands up and the jeep stopped in front of him. A WAAF Corporal was driving it.

'Blimey – a woman driver,' he said under his breath, remembering the night of the caves when Kate had driven them home in Uncle John's Austin 8. He'd felt sick for days.

The Corporal kept her face impassive as Charlie walked over to her. She'd never seen anything so funny since watching the Keystone Cops in the Cinema. He looked like an under-stuffed scarecrow with enormous painted purple lips.

'Are you local?' the Corporal asked him, keeping her voice level. 'I'm looking for Fowlmere.'

Rose and Charlie stared at her with their mouths open.

An hour later, the Corporal, against all her better judgement, deposited the children at the guard-room at Fowlmere. She was exhausted by Charlie's constant questions about the RAF and she never, ever, wanted to hear the name Rob Adams again. She felt she could write a biography about a man whose existence she hadn't known about an hour earlier. She saluted thankfully to the Duty Officer and drove off quickly.

The officer was totally bemused by having two twig-covered, purple-lipped children in his office. He went by the book and there were no regulations covering children on RAF stations.

'This is most irregular,' he said to Charlie. Rose was already curled up on two chairs, fast asleep.

Charlie looked around the Nissen hut with its corrugated roof. It had one desk, one telephone and one officer with a pile of papers in front of him.

'Don't think much of this.'

'I beg your pardon?'

'This station. Not got a lot in it. Where're the planes?' Charlie was staring out of the hut, longing for a glimpse of Rob and his Spitfire. 'What's that?' He'd seen a tall, rectangular Braithwaite water-tower in the distance, erected to control fires.

'Your parents know you've absconded, do they?'

'What?'

The officer didn't know what to do. He couldn't report the matter to the CO – he was sleeping. He flicked desperately through his book of regulations. There was nothing – nothing in it at all about children. This situation was not supposed to happen. He took out a large handkerchief and wiped his face.

'Well?' Charlie was still waiting for an answer.

The telephone rang. He watched the officer's harassed face as he answered the call. Bet he's never been up in a plane, thought Charlie, listening to him talking about duty rosters. The man put the telephone down and looked at Charlie as if he'd only just seen him.

'This cannot be happening. This is an RAF station. Children are not allowed on airfields.'

'But we're here and I want to see Flying Officer Adams.'

The officer got up and started pacing up and down. 'Well, you can't … it's not in regulations.'

Charlie watched him for some time and set his jaw. 'I won't go 'til I see Rob.'

The man turned to Charlie with an anguished face. 'Look, we're at war. Don't you understand? You can't come here to see anyone.'

'But I have and I'm not moving 'til I see Rob.' Charlie folded his arms across his chest and stared at the floor.

The officer made a strangulated sound in his throat and strode out. Charlie got up and saw him marching across the field to another hut and disappear inside it.

A few minutes later, the Duty Officer reappeared with another officer in tow. Charlie watched the broader of the two men amble across the grass towards him, a brown pipe stuck firmly between his lips. He looked important. Charlie's stomach contracted, but he wasn't going to move. Not until he'd seen Rob.

Donald Harrison sighed as he walked into the guard-room. He'd just been going to have his lunch when Palmer, the Duty Officer, flapped into the Mess and told him some cock and bull story about two purple-lipped children sitting in his office. He stopped short when he saw the wraith-like creatures in front of him: one sleeping, one very much awake. He looked at Palmer who looked back at him as if to say, I told you so.

'Well, now, laddie. I'm the Medical Officer here. Palmer tells me you won't budge from this office.' Harrison puffed on his pipe as he waited for Charlie's answer.

Charlie stood squarely in front of the man, folded his arms tightly across his chest again and looked up at him defiantly.

'No, I won't.'

The MO sat down and smiled at him. 'Oh, aye, is that a fact? ... Well, you'd better sit down then, hadn't you, and tell me all about it.'

Charlie was so surprised that he did; he told him about the farm; about running away; about trying to find his big brother.

'Oh ... you're Rob's little brother, are you?' The MO tilted his head in disbelief as he looked into Charlie's hazel eyes. Charlie went red with embarrassment. He could tell that Rob had told the Medical Officer all about him.

'Well now, Charlie, Robert isn't due back until this afternoon.'

Charlie looked at him in confusion. 'Due back? He's flying, isn't he?'

Harrison looked at the Duty Officer who shook his head.

'He had forty-eight hours' leave.'

Charlie felt as if someone had punched him in the stomach. He couldn't speak.

'Are you all right, laddie?' The MO was worried by the sudden lack of colour on the boy's face. 'When did you last eat?'

'Dunno.'

'Well, I'll tell you what we're going to do. We're going over to the cook-house while the Duty Officer telephones your parents.' He looked across at Palmer. 'Won't take you very long, Derek. Sure you won't mind.'

'You can't do that!' Charlie shouted.

The MO took the pipe out of his mouth. 'Is that so? – and why not?'

The long silence in the room was suddenly pierced by the shrill sound of the telephone.

The Duty Officer picked it up quickly, his face clouding before he turned to Donald Harrison. 'They're coming back, Sir. They might need you. Seems to be a spot of bother.'

The MO rushed out of the door and suddenly, Charlie could hear the distant drone of returning Spitfires. Rose woke up with a start and looked around wildly.

'Charlie?'

'I'm here.' His nose was pressed against the window trying to see the planes. He felt desolate.

The Duty Officer turned to Charlie before he left the office. 'Don't move from this room.'

'What's happening?' Rose asked, standing next to him to stare out of the same window.

'The squadron's coming back.'

Her face lit up. 'Then we'll see Colin and Rob.'

'No, we won't. Rob's not here. He's on leave.'

She looked at Charlie's face. 'I thought he was coming to see you.'

'So did I,' he said in a tight voice.

'Perhaps he did, but we were in the woods.'

Charlie was suddenly ecstatic. 'Yeah, never thought of that!'

The air was full of the loud drone of Spitfires, landing on the grass in the distance. Charlie ran to the door. The last time he was so excited was at the fair when he was nine; he'd hit three bulls-eyes with three darts and a man had given him a toy pony. His little brother Alfie had never slept without it afterwards.

Outside the huts, the ground-crew and pilots from B flight stood watching the Spitfires land. They all heard the choke and splutter of a faltering engine before they saw white smoke streaming from the exhaust stubs of a damaged Spitfire as it approached the field. Charlie rushed onto the grass. No one noticed him. Everyone's eyes were glued onto the Spitfire circling the field – a riddle of bullet holes clearly visible down the side of the fuselage. The pilot was desperately trying to land.

Rose rushed up to him. 'Is he going to crash?'

But Charlie couldn't hear. He was watching the wheels and flaps descend and the Spitfire turn into the wind. It was 400 feet from the ground when the engine caught fire – too low for the pilot to bale-out. Everyone held their breath as the Spitfire skimmed the branches of a tree, sailed straight through some telephone wires and convulsed with flames. A fire engine and blood wagon clanged towards the plane as the pilot dived headlong over the side of the cockpit. The Spitfire careered along the field at 45 mph and tipped over on its nose. The petrol tank blew up. Everyone ignored the inferno of flames as they ran towards the pilot who lay on the field; his oxygen mask covering his face; his Mae West inflated and one arm twisted at a strange angle to his body.

Donald Harrison, the Medical Officer ripped the oxygen mask off the pilot's face and Charlie felt the razor-edge of Rose's nails penetrate his palm as they saw Colin lying on the grass.

Chapter 31

'We travel in order to come home.'

James Carlisle
The Feather Bed, 1906

'We don't get many children in this hospital,' said the ample Sister McPherson, smiling down at the strange duo in front of her. The little lass's eyes were swollen from crying. 'Your brother's a very lucky young man, dear. He's a bit dazed – had concussion, but he's only got a broken arm after that fall. The Medical Officer told me that he has his Mae West to thank for that.'

Sister McPherson was feeling very well disposed towards the children. The MO Donald Harrison was just the sort of man who could make her feel well disposed towards anybody: a broad, bonny, pipe-smoking Scot, just like her father. He'd sat in her office having a cup of tea and talking with her for well over fifteen minutes. At first about the children, telling her that he had contacted Charlie's foster father; then he'd asked her to go to a concert with him, that very week.

'He's not going to die, is he?' said Rose, sobbing. 'My Mum would never get over it.'

Charlie put his arm around Rose's shoulder and squeezed it.

'The nurse said he's all right, Rose.'

The Sister's face hardly tightened at all. 'It's Sister, dear, not nurse.'

'Sorry, Sister.' Charlie smiled up at her. She smiled back. He would be handsome lad when he was older she could see.

'Would you like to see him?'

Rose stopped crying immediately. 'Could we?'

'As long as you don't stay too long and upset him.'

'She won't upset him, Sister.'

The Sister looked down into Charlie's face and nodded. She felt she could trust him to keep the lassie under control.

'Can I have a wash first, Sister?' Rose asked her.

'You both can,' she answered, looking at the debris of twigs and leaves in their hair and the stains around their mouths. She pointed to a washroom in the distance.

After they'd washed and tried to remove most of the twigs and leaves, they followed the Sister's large dark-blue uniformed figure down a tunnel of flaking white-painted corridors until they reached a small room. Colin lay on the narrow hospital bed with his eyes closed; his left arm in plaster and his face the colour of clay; large, orange freckles stood out in relief.

'Two minutes,' the Sister said, looking at Charlie.

Colin's eyes fluttered open and he saw two small ghosts standing at the side of his bed. One of them looked like his sister. Perhaps I'm dead already, he thought as he closed his eyes.

'Colin,' Rose whispered.

His eyes fluttered open again in astonishment. It *was* Rose.

Tears started to drip down her cheeks.

'Oh, Blimey – not again.' Charlie was getting fed up. Girls seemed to cry at everything.

'What the hell are you kids doing in an RAF hospital?' Colin tried to lift up his left arm and groaned.

'Sorry, Col – we've run away. Didn't like it there. Are you all right? You're not in pain, are you?'

Colin focused on his sister. What was she talking about? Not in pain?

'Never felt better, Dumbo. Now push off.' He closed his eyes again.

Rose grinned at him. He'd never talk to her like that if he was going to die.

The Duty Officer was back amongst his papers. Far easier to deal with than people. He was relieved by the fact that he no longer had any responsibility, whatsoever, for looking after the children. The MO had allowed them to travel with him in the ambulance. Most irregular, but then, he often found Donald Harrison irregular. However, the episode was now closed.

He was deep into his paper-work and didn't hear the squeal of brakes outside the guard-room until the door was suddenly flung back, and two middle-aged women almost ran into his room. It was unbelievable. Where were all these civilians coming from?

'Have you seen two children?' Mary asked him.

He got up. 'Yes, Madam. I have, but thank goodness they've gone to hospital.'

'Hospital?' Hilda screamed.

The Duty Officer shuddered. He hated hysterical women.

'Yes, Madam. Hospital with one of our pilots who –' He stopped himself in time. Good heavens, he didn't even know who these women were.

Both women had gone pale. This is probably the worst day of my life, Palmer thought. First, cheeky, unkempt children, now hysterical, middle-aged women.

'There wasn't a crash, was there?' Mary asked him quietly.

He looked into Mary's steady brown eyes. 'Yes, but no one was seriously hurt, Madam. Look, really, I can't spend any more time talking to civilians. The children are at Greengage Cottage hospital – two miles down that road.' He pointed the way, but Mary and Hilda were already rushing for the door. He watched them drive off in a cloud of dust.

'Well, thank you very much for all the information, Duty Officer Palmer. You've been most helpful … Don't mention it, Madam. Only too happy to waste most of the day talking to civilians.' He slowly ground his pen into one of the papers on his desk.

By the time Mary and Hilda reached the hospital it was five o'clock. They'd had no food all day and were both feeling light-headed as they walked through the main entrance.

'I can't believe it, Mary. After two days – to find them in a hospital.'

'I know.'

They felt completely exhausted as a nurse showed them into Sister McPherson's office.

'Mrs Adams and Mrs Brazier, Sister. The children's mothers.'

The Sister waved them into chairs. 'Good afternoon, ladies. Which of you is Mrs Brazier?'

'I am – what is it?' Hilda felt all the blood rush from her head.

'What a relief, eh? Your son and daughter safe in the same hospital.'

Hilda looked at her in confusion. 'Colin's here as well?'

Sister McPherson explained about Colin's crash, adding that he would obviously have to convalesce at home. Hilda's face glowed after the Sister had told her the injuries were superficial.

'Where are the children, Sister?' Mary was worried about seeing Charlie. What would she do? How would he feel?

The Sister turned to the calm, elegant, woman in front of her. 'They're having something to eat. I don't think they're eaten anything for days.'

Hilda and Mary looked at each other. Neither had they.

'Could we see them now, Sister?'

Sister McPherson was just about to explain the rules of the hospital when she looked at the women's faces; she was startled by the emotional hunger she saw. 'I'll show you where the canteen is.'

Like Charlie and Rose earlier, they followed Sister McPherson's ample figure down the myriad of corridors until they came to a stark, white room with trestle tables. Along one wall, the hospital cooks were ladling out food. Mary pressed a hand over her heart, trying to still its erratic rhythm. On a table, at the far side of the room, they saw two small, dishevelled figures gulping down food.

Hilda and Mary both began to cry.

'The children are perfectly all right, ladies,' the Sister assured them, then suddenly realised that neither woman was listening to her. They were looking at Charlie and Rose with such love in their eyes that her own started watering. She walked swiftly away.

Mary and Hilda continued to watch the children eating their food. Neither of them had realised how frightened they were until they saw them safe. Suddenly, Charlie looked up and saw Mary staring at him. He jumped up, almost knocking Rose off the bench as he ran across the room and threw his arms around her, sobbing. Rose followed, close on his heels. The women rocked the children in their arms, all of them crying, while the hospital staff looked on in astonishment.

Chapter 32

'There is only one happiness in life;
to love and be loved.'

George Sand (1804-1876)

Mary parked the car near Silver Street Bridge in Cambridge and they all got out, laughing. The servicemen and women walking past them, stared, wondering at the happiness they could see on their faces.

'The last time I saw someone that happy,' a passing Corporal said to his girl friend, 'was when my old man won 200 nicker on the horses.'

Mary and Charlie were walking hand-in-hand along the pavement towards Laundress Lane. She looked down into Charlie's beaming face and beamed back at him. She had never realised how much she'd wanted him to want her until she'd seen him flying across the room towards her. She looked across at Rose, hanging on to her mother's arm. They had told the children in the car that they weren't going to send them away again. They were going to come home. Mary had had to stop the car when she saw the ecstatic expression on Charlie's face. War had tainted everything, but it had given her that look.

At the Mill end of Laundress Lane they walked past a sign that read: *No Thoroughfare for Carriages or Horses, 24th March, 1857.* The first time Mary had seen that sign she was on her honeymoon with John. Twenty-three years ago. It was impossible to believe that so much time had disappeared. Britain was at war, but at that moment, she was more happy than she'd been for years, holding Charlie's hand; knowing he wanted to hold hers.

Mary had made a number of telephone calls before they left the hospital. She'd spoken to John and asked him to contact Hilda's husband and then she'd rung *Avonside*. She and John had walked past the small thatched Tudor cottage, which offered bed and breakfast, all those years ago. They had stood and admired the crowded flowerbeds surrounding it, before seeing the hundreds of gnomes standing in the garden, admiring them too. The owners had built a miniature world for them. They had four wells, six swings, twenty-five houses and numerous bridges they could walk over. They had both roared with laughter at the sight, then John had turned to her and said: 'if we ever come back to Cambridge, Mary, we'll stay here – if they treat gnomes this well, imagine how well they treat their guests.' They had been back three times and it was true. They were treated like Royalty.

'We're here.'

Rose and Charlie were enchanted with the miniature world and crouched down in the garden with the gnomes while Mary and Hilda went to see Mr and Mrs Foster.

Mary had warned Hilda about their appearance. The elderly couple greeted Mary like a long-lost friend when they answered the door. Mary's eyes darted in Hilda's direction; she could see her trying to control her face. Mr and Mrs Foster looked exactly like their garden gnomes: small, rotund, with large, wide, welcoming smiles. Mr Foster was even wearing the same sort of small wire glasses and brown trousers as the gnomes.

Hilda stared intently at the sparkling glassware displayed on numerous shelves in the lounge, as Mary told them everything that had happened. The couple looked out of the window and were delighted to see Charlie and Rose sitting in the garden admiring the gnomes.

'A Spitfire pilot you say?' The elderly couple couldn't have looked more surprised if two angels had appeared in their living room. 'And how is young Robert?'

'Oh, he's fine. He'll be here soon.'

The couple beamed at Mary. Rob had been fifteen when he had first stayed with them.

Hilda collapsed back into the comfort of the Foster's chintz-covered settee and was soon asleep.

'Oh dear, I hope it's not something we said,' Mrs Foster's long-sighted blue eyes crinkled in concern as she looked at Mary.

'No, of course not, Mrs Foster. It's the strain of the last few days.'

The Fosters made soothing, clucking noises before rushing to make them some tea.

Charlie and Rose were still sitting in the garden when Rob's car stopped outside the cottage. Charlie looked up and saw dark-brown curly hair bobbing along the hedge.

'Rob!' he screamed, almost knocking over two gnomes on a bridge as he ran down the garden path. 'How did you find us?'

Rob, still tired and stressed from his night with Billie and the Blitz, braced himself for the onslaught of Charlie's small body hurtling itself towards him – a grin almost splitting his face.

'God!' He gasped as the air was knocked out of his lungs. 'Like being attacked by the Hun.' He held Charlie by the shoulders, looking down into his hazel eyes. 'Why did you run away? You scared the living daylights out of Mum and Dad.'

Charlie looked up him. 'Did you go to see me – at the farm?'

Rob shook his head and Charlie's grin froze.

'I didn't have –'

'Hello, Rob. Have you seen Colin? He was nearly killed.' Rose walked towards him with a big grin on her face.

Rob was still looking at Charlie.

'Yes, I've just come from the hospital. I must see Aunt Mary, Charlie. I'll talk to you later.'

Charlie stared at the gnomes.

Mr and Mrs Foster were thrilled to see Rob in uniform and fluttered about giving him tea and scones. He grinned at his mother as they walked backwards out of the room, almost bowing to Rob. They closed the door quietly behind them.

'They think I'm going to win the war single-handedly,' he whispered as he walked over to his mother and gave her a big hug.

Hilda had taken the children upstairs to give Mary and Rob some time together.

Mary leaned back to look into her son's face.

'What's the matter, darling? You look really drained.' Now they were alone, she could see the strain in Rob's eyes.

Rob told his mother about the night in London: going to Shepherd's pub and meeting Billie; about the explosion and the hospital. He omitted the scene in the bedroom.

'Is the girl all right?'

'Yes, she's very lucky … I told her I had to go back to the squadron.'

There was a small silence.

'Will you see her again?'

'I don't know … I shouldn't think so.'

'What about Kate?'

'What about her?'

'Well, I thought you were … fond of her.'

'I am.'

Mary heard the crack of his knuckles across the room.

'If only you could come home and get some rest.'

Rob laid his head back on the chintz-covered settee. 'Wish I could too … What are you going to do about Charlie?'

'He's coming home with me.'

'Dad said all the schools have closed.'

'I know – I'll think of something.'

He smiled at his mother. 'Yes, you always do.'

'I wish I'd never let him go to the farm. They were working him to death, Rob. You ought to have seen the family.'

'I meant to. I promised Charlie.' He looked around at the familiar room. 'Some things never change with time, do they?' They smiled at each other, remembering their last holiday together. 'Mum – I'm due back on the base in an hour.'

'An hour?' Mary's face clouded. 'But you look so tired, darling.'

'Oh, I'll be okay … once the old adrenalin's rushing round the body.' He smiled at her.

'They expect so much from you pilots.'

'It's called war, Mum.'

In the silence they could hear the children creaking over the ancient floorboards above their heads.

She looked at him. 'It's a pity politicians enjoy playing war games.'

'It's not a game.'

Another silence.

'I know.' She smiled brightly. 'Well, we've all had an eventful few days, but at least Colin's safe.'

Rob noted the tight expression on his Mother's face.

'When are you going home?'

'In a couple of days. Hilda wants to visit Colin again and I want to show Charlie Cambridge.'

'Five years ago you were showing it to me.'

Mary could feel tears near the surface of her eyes. 'Yes, I know.'

They could hear Charlie upstairs shouting to Rose to look at something. They smiled at each other.

'Anyway – I'm glad Col's okay. You know what he said to me at the hospital? ... He's thinking of taking up nihilism.'

'What?'

'But only part-time.' Rob laughed. 'When his favourite nurse is off-duty and the Sister forces him to eat the hospital food. He's looking forward to his Mum's cooking.'

'Missing mine too, are you?'

They smiled at each other again.

'Don't worry about me, Mum. I've got fast reflexes.'

Mary's smile faded.

'I'd like to talk to Charlie before I go – would you mind?'

'You're very fond of him, aren't you?'

'So are you. Travelling all over the country to find him. You know something – I can hardly remember a time before Charlie.'

They both smiled again. Briefly.

'I'll call him.' Mary walked towards the door, then turned back suddenly. 'You will be careful, won't you, darling?'

'Oh, I'll keep a weather-eye open, Mum, don't you worry,' Rob said lightly.

Charlie and Rob were standing on Silver Street Bridge, looking down into the water. They could see a few people punting down the river – their distant voices drifting up to them. A scene of pre-war tranquillity. Rob soaked it up.

'I couldn't come to see you, Charlie. I was caught in an air-raid in London.' This time Rob omitted Billie altogether.

'You really were going to come to see me?' Charlie looked closely into Rob's dark brown eyes, so much like Auntie Mary's.

'I certainly was. I even told Oscar.' He put his arm round Charlie's shoulder as they walked over the bridge, telling him about Oscar's vast knowledge of the pilots in Fighter Command.

'Blimey – hope Hitler doesn't get to hear about him.' Charlie looked worried.

'Oh, Charlie,' Rob said, laughing.

'What?'

'Nothing.' They walked past the Victorian baroque architecture of the Fitzwilliam Museum towards Peterhouse. Rob had always been fascinated by it ever since he'd discovered the film star James Mason had acted there in the undergraduate theatre and managed to get a First at the same time. He kept imagining him learning his lines as he walked under the colonnades. They walked past the porter's lodge into the seclusion and harmony of the chapel arcade.

Charlie looked around in awe. 'This is a bit old, isn't it?'

'Just a bit. Thirteenth century, I think. Come on let's walk over to the chapel.'

'We're not going in, are we? Don't like churches. Not after what happened to Rose.'

'No, let's just sit on the grass.' Rob looked at his watch as they walked over and sat down. He had to leave in half-an-hour.

'Charlie – I want you to do something for me.'

'What?'

'Look after Auntie Mary. She's worried about us.'

'Of course I'll look after her, but I don't know why she's worried about me. I don't do nothing worrying.'

Rob laughed and Charlie looked at him in astonishment. 'What?'

Rob's laughter faded fast. 'I've got to leave soon.'

Charlie's lip quivered.

'Rob? … do you ever feel … frightened … when you're flying?'

'Often. Only a coward boasts he's never afraid.'

'Then what makes someone brave?'

Rob sighed as he looked up at the scudding clouds, searching for the right words.

'I think … someone who's frightened of doing something he knows he must do – not for himself – but for other people … but still does it.'

They looked at each other without speaking, then Rob put his hand inside his jacket pocket and brought out the blue stone Charlie had given him a year ago. He held it out to Charlie.

'Here, keep this safe 'til you see me again.'

Charlie pressed the stone into his palm.

'Come on,' Rob said, pulling Charlie to his feet. 'I'll got to say goodbye to Mum.'

Mary fought back tears as she walked down the path with Rob towards his car.

'Bye, darling. Take care.'

'I will. Don't worry,' Rob said, as he swung himself into the car. The others were standing at the garden gate, waving wildly to him. Charlie rushed down the path at the last minute.

'Give the Hun hell, Rob!'

'I'll try, little brother, I'll try,' Rob shouted as he drove off.

Charlie didn't hear what Mary was saying to him. Rob's words kept ringing in his ears. He let out a great whoop of joy and threw his arms around her.

Chapter 33

'Thus the whirligig
of time brings in his revenges'

William Shakespeare (1564-1616)
Twelfth Night

The water was icy when Rob hit it; he was pulled under the waves by the monster shroud of his parachute. Water rushed up his nose and into his mouth. He wanted to relax into the cushion of death, but faces kept wavering in front of him: Kate on the pier; Charlie in the caves; his parents in the garden. Then he was kicking; fighting the parachute which pulled him towards extinction. Spluttering to the surface, he drank in deep draughts of fresh air. Then the sobs came at the thought of what he must do before the waterlogged parachute dragged him to the bottom of the ocean.

He held his breath as his incinerated fingers twisted the metal disc to release the parachute. His screams shocked the seagulls who'd been flapping for food; they swooped away over the sea.

Rob watched in horror as pieces of his flesh flaked off into bloody water.

He had been in the water for days or was it hours or only minutes? He couldn't tell. It was hysterically funny: he was in the middle of the North Sea, burnt to a cinder, but his Mae West hadn't been burnt at all. He could hear his laughter roll along the miles and miles of flat, empty ocean.

‘Who God wishes to destroy, he first makes mad,’ he shouted to a passing seagull. He wouldn’t last long. Not if he was mad. But what if he wasn’t? What if he was only pretending to be mad like Hamlet or Kafka? Perhaps he could turn himself into a seagull and fly away. He roared with laughter. Did Heathcliff kill Hindley? Had the motive. Had the time. Was the water getting colder or the sun disappearing? Or the water disappearing and the sun getting colder? He couldn’t tell. He lifted his mutilated hands out of the water and looked at them. Who did they belong to?

‘Frying tonight. I’m frying tonight, birdie, or is it afternoon? Where’s the sun gone? Burning. Burning. Burning Bright. Like a star … like a diamond in the ...’

Voices. Darkness. Rocking. Rock a bye baby. Drift. Drift. Drift into … Pain. A Poker. White. Hot. Hotter. Screams. Loud. Louder. SOMEONE. SOMEWHERE WAS PEELING OFF HIS SKIN.

Chapter 34

'Mortality, behold and fear!
What a change of flesh is here!'

Francis Beaumont (1584-1616)
After seeing the tombs at Westminster Abbey

'nk.'

The saliva between Rob's lips was as tacky as boiled rice water. He had the word clearly in his head, but somewhere in his throat it got confused. A young face in nurse's uniform wavered above him.

'nk!' he said louder.

She shook her head and disappeared. Someone had taken out his tongue and given him a dehydrated elephant's.

'Ink!' he screamed.

A crackle of starch. Sister Massie lifted up his head a little and put a spout between his swollen lips. From the corner of his eye he could see a lump of flesh, trying to suck like a baby. Cool lemonade saturated his mouth. He swallowed it slowly. The Sister frowned as she concentrated on holding the spouted cup and his head steady. Their eyes met for a split second. For a split second, Rob saw the revulsion in her face. He fell back heavily on the bed, sobbing; pain exploding through his body.

A hypodermic needle made the room sway.

A pinprick of light in the distance. Red. He looked down the tunnel of a hospital bed. Two arms were propped up in front of him. He wondered what the black claws were doing at the end of them. Flickering pictures in slow motion: an old woman in uniform knitting at night; a small boy touching him; faces peering; mouths moving silently in smiles; needles floating in ether. A woman weeping. Flames crucifying his body. The terrible pungency of flesh. And the unquenchable thirst that went on and on and on.

Mary sat still on a hospital chair in a small white room. The smell of ether was stronger in here. She still hadn't got used to it, even after all this time. Rob's arms were supported by straps attached to the ceiling and covered from elbow to fingers in tannic acid. The lower part of his face was covered with white gauze. It had been a quiet day, relatively speaking. He hadn't screamed so much. He'd been moved to an RAF hospital in the country after the lifeboat had rescued him from the North Sea. The journey had been a nightmare of pain for him. And her. She was waiting for the time when she could talk to him; when he could listen. He'd been rambling in a morphine-induced nightmare for weeks while the Luftwaffe carried on bombing London. She looked out of the window as she did every day. Every day as Rob screamed out his nightmares, she had sat watching the leaves changing colour.

'There's a kaleidoscope outside your window, darling. Your favourite season,' she repeatedly told her mutilated son as they jabbed more morphine into his body.

The late September sun streamed through the window and formed a crown round Mary's white hair. It had taken a week for her hair to change colour, just like the leaves. The autumn of her life. John had told her it was a fallacy that shock could turn hair white overnight; sometimes hair fell out after shock, leaving greying hair which did turn white. He'd had to go home after two weeks. She knew that. He had patients to look after.

She had always been so proud of her curly brown hair; now it seemed an irrelevance, like a limb that was never used. She watched Rob jerking repeatedly in his sleep. The doctors had warned her that the morphine would make him jerk and twitch. She had become used to it over the weeks. She thought she might get used to his face too. In time. They told her Rob was lucky. At least his eyes weren't damaged. Not like some of the other pilots she had seen and heard in the hospital. Lucky. Oh, the irony of fate: the perfection of his large brown eyes made his disfigurement far worse. Eyes which sometimes recognised her through the swirling mists of morphine.

She found his hands difficult to look at. 'Black claws! Black claws crawling over me, Charlie!' he kept shouting in his sleep. What could he possibly do with such hands? The tannic acid made them black. But it wasn't the colour which disturbed Mary so much as the bird-like claws they'd become; claws that were burrowing into his palms. The doctors had warned her that he would never fly again.

Mary heard the nurses walking towards the room and her stomach tightened as she thought of the agony Rob would have to endure as they changed his dressings. The third change that day. And it took an hour. Sister Massie and a young VAD Red Cross nurse swung the door open. They both smiled at Mary; she smiled back, automatically. Her father would have been so proud of her observance of social etiquette.

'I'll come back later,' she said, heading for the door before they could speak. She couldn't bear to hear him screaming. Not again.

Mary was surprised to find the sun was still shining when she walked out of the hospital. There was a small park opposite. She would sit there. People were laughing in the distance. As if nothing had happened. She sat on a park bench and watched the wind swirl September leaves: tobacco and copper and gold helter-skeltered round an oak tree. She opened her handbag and fingered items she didn't need: a broken pen, a piece of paper with the word ROB written on it, a large, round mirror … and there, lying at the bottom of her bag … the letter. The letter she'd written to Kate weeks ago. The letter that told her Rob's face had been lost in a fire. The letter she *had* sent dismissed his burns in a line and concentrated on Rob's miraculous good fortune. A British convoy had been sailing in Rob's vicinity in the North Sea when a young, eagle-eyed Naval Officer in the first ship had spotted something in the water – Rob's unconscious body barely afloat in his Mae West. The convoy had been immediately alerted and altered course to avoid running him down. Once aboard, the ship's surgeon had wrapped Rob's burnt body in blankets to counteract the shock and he was transported by naval helicopter to a military hospital. He was lying in a hospital bed within hours of being picked up. Rob was so lucky to be alive, Mary had written. So why do I feel dead inside? She wondered.

She put the letter she had never sent Kate back in the bottom of her bag and sat watching the leaves. She wanted to weep for the loss of her son's face: a face that once caught the last seconds of the sun.

An hour later, her feet moved in slow motion down the corridor towards Rob's room, trying to blot out the moment: the moment when she wouldn't see her son again.

As she opened the door she saw something lying on the bed with its eyes open. Was that really Rob? For the first time in weeks he turned and looked at her. Really looked at her.

'Hello, darling.'

'Lo, Mum. What happened to your hair?'

'Changed colour while you were sleeping.'

'Bit like my hands.'

Mary's stomach muscles contracted as Rob stared down at the black claws.

'These hands won't fly again, will they, Mum?'

'The doctors have told me about a skin graft specialist. Mr McIndoe. He can do wonders.'

'What – make new hands?'

'No, but he can treat them so that they won't be so –'

'Hideous?'

'No … better.'

'What about my face? I can see my lips, Mum – without a mirror. Where are the mirrors in this hospital, for Christ's sake?' He started to get out of bed.

'Rob! Don't!' Mary ran to the door and threw it open, shouting for a nurse as Rob lurched across the room to a mirror hidden in an alcove. He found himself facing a monster with a ravaged face swollen to twice its normal size. It had black claws dangling from the end of its arms. But the horror was – it looked at him with his own eyes. The floor hit him hard as he crashed into it.

Chapter 35

'Tis all a Chequer-board of Nights and Days
Where Destiny with Men for Pieces plays...'

The Rubáiyát of Omar Khayyám, XLIX

Charlie had persuaded Mary and John to let him see Rob, even though he was in a morphine-induced nightmare. He told them he wouldn't leave the hospital until he'd seen him. They knew he meant it. The first time they had walked into the room with him, they had held his hands, but nothing could have prepared him for the sight that was waiting for him: the grotesque distortion of a face tormented by fire. But Charlie had only held their hands tighter as he walked towards the burnt body. They had tried to touch Rob with love; all he felt was pain. But gradually, over the weeks, Kate's words had touched him. She had written to Rob every day because she couldn't visit him. Rob couldn't open the letters, but asked Charlie to open them for him; then he held them in front of Rob's face. Rob never commented on what he read and Charlie never asked, but he always seemed a little more cheerful after he'd read them – at least for an hour.

Then he looked into a mirror.

Rob lay on his bed staring at the ceiling with a glazed expression in his eyes. He was retreating from life and Charlie knew it. Now Kate's numerous letters lay ignored in the hospital locker. Charlie took a deep breath, trying to control the shaking in his hands as he took out a letter at random and read.

'*Dear Rob –*'

'What are you doing?' Rob's voice was shrill with anger.

'Your mother wrote to me about your accident …' Charlie carried on reading, not knowing what Rob would do.

'How dare you read my letter!'

'I can't imagine the pain you're suffering –'

'Give it to me!'

'I don't even know if you can read this by –'

'Of course I fucking can't!'

'I've been desperately trying to get leave to see you, but I've been posted to Wales and the "powers that be" say that as you're not a relative, etc... you know what they're like …'

Charlie couldn't move, could hardly hold the letter. Rob was creeping along the bed towards him.

'You must be in pain, so I won't write reams. I just wanted to tell you –'

'Stop reading! Look at me!'

Rob's gigantic head was inches away from Charlie's: an obscene gargoyle, glaring at him.

'What do I look like?'

Terrifying words shot into Charlie's mind.

'Well? Rob shouted in his face. 'You always say what's in your mind! Tell me!'

Charlie's body was braced for flight, but he couldn't move. Couldn't speak.

'You can't answer because I'm a fucking freak, aren't I?'

'Yes!' Charlie screamed.

A sudden whirl of leaves played outside the window as Rob crashed back onto the bed, crushed by pain. Charlie knew that the next words he spoke might be the most important ones he ever said, but he didn't know what they were.

'Rob … Kate says she loves you whatever's happened to you.'

Rob made a strangulated sound in his throat, waiting for the pain to subside. 'What the hell do you know about love?' he whispered. 'Kate loves someone who doesn't exist any more.'

'You do! You're still Rob … you just don't look like him. Not yet.'

Rob turned his gigantic head towards the wall and was silent.

Charlie was frightened; he knew he must persuade him to have some plastic surgery soon or he would look like a gargoyle for the rest of his life. Archie McIndoe, the plastic surgeon, had told them two days ago. He had also warned them of the pain Rob would have to endure if he agreed.

'Wish someone loved me like Kate loves you.'

Rob made a sound like an animal caught on a wire and Charlie wanted to be sick.

'Aunt Mary's talked to this doctor, Rob. He's good. He can help you. He can make your face and hands better. Aunt Mary says.'

A violent shiver ran through Charlie's body. What if he never replied? Ever? What would he do? Long minutes limped by.

At last a toneless voice muttered. 'Don't believe it.'

'You don't believe your Mum?'

'No,' Rob turned his disfigured face towards Charlie, 'I don't believe the Doctor.'

'Why would he lie?'

'Leave me alone!'

'I won't. Not 'til you see this doctor. It's not going to hurt you to see him, is it? Other pilots in the hospital have seen him. I've talked to them.'

'I don't care a fuck about other pilots!'

Charlie felt an iron hand squeeze his chest. 'What about Kate? You care about her, don't you? Do you want her to see you like this?'

Rob didn't answer. He was remembering Kate on the pier with her beautiful chestnut hair flying round her face as she smiled at him. Would she ever smile at him like that again?

'If you don't like your face – change it! All you've got to do is see this doctor? It's not going to hurt to see him, is it?'

'There's no point! My face is too burnt and look at my hands for Christ's sake – they're claws! I can't even go to the bloody lavatory by myself!'

Charlie was getting desperate. He must make Rob see a future.

'Well, you would, if you had these operations!'

'I've had enough pain. Just leave me alone to die, that's all I ask.'

Charlie started pacing up and down the room.

'Oh is that all! … Is that all.' His heavy breathing agitated the air.

'Well, this is a true story this is. There was this boy called Rob. Lived by the sea – with his Mum and Dad in a big house – had everything. A big bike. Big bedroom. Big telescope. Every night he could look up at the stars. His Mum and Dad did everything for him because they loved him lots, see.'

'Charlie –'

'Then one day a war started and Rob joined the RAF and became a pilot and they were so proud of him.'

'Charlie! –'

'Then another day a dirty boy from London come to live in his house and Rob's Dad made him clean. And this boy – couldn't read and write 'cos his Dad said: "No fuckin' use you is." Said it every night, he did. When he hit him. With a belt. Again and again and again! Tied him up and hit him on the soles of his feet sometimes. No one would look there, would they?'

'Charlie, don't!' Rob's eyes were following him as he paced up and down the room, talking faster and faster.

'This boy liked his new home – 'cos Rob showed him the stars and books and – and pictures and planes and – and how to be brave, but one day this boy found out – Rob was a – was a – f-f-fuckin' liar 'cos he didn't care – didn't care a toss about no one – just himself – didn't care about his Mum or Dad – just himself – just his f-f-fuckin' self – and his Mum got thinner and thinner – and he never noticed – and one day she died 'cos she found out her son was a selfish … stupid … f-f-fuckin' coward and … and … and …'

And suddenly Charlie slumped onto the floor. His thin shoulders shaking convulsively with sobs.

Rob sat up slowly in the bed. His hands twitching. He watched Charlie's shoulders heaving and felt his sobs deep inside his body.

'Charlie … You've got to change the ending of the story.'

The sobbing subsided slowly and an endless silence filled the room.

Charlie turned towards Rob and said, 'No … you've got to.'

A long, drawn-out sigh escaped from between Rob's twisted lips as he concentrated on the beauty of one blue hill in the distance beyond the window for a long, long time.

Charlie's eyes never left his face.

At last, Rob whispered, 'All right – go and tell Mum … I'll see the specialist.'

'And what about Kate?'

Rob's mouth moved grotesquely before he could speak. 'Write her a letter, Charlie.'

'Saying what?'

'Saying … saying …'

Charlie reached inside his short, grey trouser pocket and brought out a notepad and waited.

'Saying … I love her.'

Charlie reached inside his pocket again. This time he brought out the blue stone and put it on the locker at the side of Rob's bed. It shimmered in the sunlight.